Contents

About the British Institute of Learning Disabilities

The British Institute of Learning Disabilities (BILD) is committed to improving the quality of life for people with a learning disability by involving them and their families in all aspects of our work, working with government and public bodies to achieve full citizenship, undertaking beneficial research and development projects and helping service providers to develop and share good practice.

BILD Publications is the imprint of:
British Institute of Learning Disabilities
Campion House
Green Street
Kidderminster
Worcestershire DY10 1JL

Telephone: 01562 723010
Fax: 01562 723029
Email: enquiries@bild.org.uk
Website: www.bild.org.uk

BILD Publications are distributed by:
BookSource
50 Cambuslang Road
Cambuslang
Glasgow G32 8NB

Telephone: 0845 370 0067
Fax: 0845 370 0068

For a publications catalogue with details of all BILD books and journals and for information about learning and qualifications services telephone 01562 723010, email enquiries@bild.org.uk or visit the BILD website www.bild.org.uk

© Kevin Chettle

Principles of
learning disability support

Induction Award

Tynnwyd o Stoc
Withdrawn from stock

Supporting people who have a learning disability

John Brooke

www.bild.org.uk
✓ Information and support
✓ Useful weblinks
✓ 24 hour online ordering

0845 370 0067

www.harcourt.co.uk
✓ Free online support
✓ Useful weblinks
✓ 24 hour online ordering

01865 888118

ild Heinemann

Heinemann is an imprint of Harcourt Education Limited, a company incorporated in England and Wales, having its registered office: Halley Court, Jordan Hill, Oxford OX2 8EJ. Registered company number: 3099304

www.harcourt.co.uk

Heinemann is the registered trademark of Harcourt Education Limited

Text © BILD 2007

First published 2007

12 11 10 09 08 07

10 9 8 7 6 5 4 3 2 1

British Library Cataloguing in Publication Data is available from the British Library on request.

ISBN 978 0 435500 01 6

Edited by Kathy Peltan
Designed and typeset by 𝒯\ Tek-Art, Croydon Surrey
Original illustrations © Harcourt Education Limited 2007
Cover illustration © Kevin Chettle
Printed in the UK by Scotprint

Acknowledgements
The author and publisher would like to thank the following individuals and organisations for permission to reproduce photographs: Page 5 – © Harcourt Education Ltd. Martin Sookias. Mencap; page 8 – © Mencap; page 13 – © PhotoDisc; page 15 – © Getty Images/PhotoDisc; page 19 – © Photofusion Picture Library/Alamy; page 21 – (a) © iStockphoto, (b) © Israel Images/Alamy, (c) © Oren Ariel/iStockphoto, (d) © PhotoDisc, (e) Israel Images/Alamy; page 22 – © Paul Doyle/Alamy; page 27 – © Harcourt Education Ltd. Gareth Boden; page 33 – © Paula Solloway/Alamy; page 35 – © Harcourt Education Ltd. Debbie Rowe; page 55 – © Mencap; page 62 – © Photofusion Picture Library/Alamy; page 77 – © Helene Rogers/Alamy.

Every effort has been made to contact copyright holders of material reproduced in this book. Any omissions will be rectified in subsequent printings if notice is given to the publishers.

Websites
The websites used in this book were correct and up to date at the time of publication. It is essential for tutors to preview each website before using it in class so as to ensure that the URL is still accurate, relevant and appropriate. We suggest that tutors bookmark useful websites and consider enabling students to access them through the school/college/satellite centre/service provider intranet.

Acknowledgements

Much of the content of this study book has been adapted from an outstanding series of previous works by Alice Bradley, published by BILD.

Three of the case studies arise from discussions with Amarjit, Annie, Carol, Elaine, Steven and Stuart, and from their support workers, Heather and June, all of whom gave generously of their time and experiences.

Mike Bentley, Barbara Coles, Annie Lawton, Robina Mallett and Nick Smith read the manuscripts and provided valuable advice.

My thanks and acknowledgements to all these, and to the many individuals with learning disabilities and their families and supporters who have taught me over the years.

We gratefully acknowledge the help of Kevin Chettle for permission to reproduce his paintings on the cover and title page. The paintings are a moving account of his life in a long-stay institution. Kevin now lives in the community and earns his living through giving lectures and selling his paintings which can be purchased through Advocacy in Action, telephone 01159 470780.

About the author

John Brooke is a freelance writer, editor and trainer. He has worked in support of people with learning disabilities of all ages, mainly in educational and community settings. His main areas of interest have been challenging behaviour, mental health and advocacy.

Introduction

induction
period of learning, shortly after starting a new job or volunteering placement

family carer
a relative of a person with learning disabilities who has an interest in their well-being

This book is for anyone beginning work with people with a learning disability. It is one of four books that will provide you with all the information you need during your **induction**. It will help you to find out more about the lives of people with learning disabilities, the service you work for and what it means to be a social care worker or volunteer. It will also be useful for personal assistants, volunteers and **family carers**, as well as for the growing number of people who are now managing their own support with money they receive through direct payments and individual budgets.

Learning disability qualifications

Common Induction Standards

All new workers in social care jobs need to know about a number of important topics during the first few weeks and months in their new job. What you need to know has been decided by Skills for Care, the strategic development organisation for the adult social care workforce in England. The topics have been set out in their Common Induction Standards (CIS). Your employer will provide a detailed induction programme that will cover:

- listening to people with learning disabilities and their families
- communicating effectively
- working safely
- your organisation's policies and procedures
- your role as a learning disability worker
- recognising and responding to abuse and neglect
- the principles of care.

The four induction books that cover all the CIS topics are:

Principles of learning disability support
Your role as a learning disability worker
Health and safety in a learning disability service
Protecting people who have a learning disability from abuse.

The Induction Award

As well as covering all the Skills for Care Common Induction Standards topics, the four books in this series also meet the requirements of the Induction Award: Supporting People who have a Learning Disability, a nationally recognised qualification appropriate for people who work in services that support people with learning disabilities.

The Induction Award helps new workers to develop knowledge and understanding. This series of books relating to the Common Induction Standards links to the Induction Award at levels 2 and 3.

Principles of learning disability support covers all the learning needed for one Induction Award unit at levels 2 and 3. Induction Award accreditation for your induction learning will be helpful to your career in supporting people with learning disabilities because:

- you will have gained certificates for achieving a national qualification
- the knowledge and understanding you have gained during your induction will help you to move on to an NVQ qualification in health and social care.

NVQ in health and social care

The National Vocational Qualifications (NVQs) in health and social care are the recognised qualifications for the entire social care sector in England, Wales and Northern Ireland, including services that support people with a learning disability. In Scotland these qualifications are known as Scottish Vocational Qualifications (SVQs). NVQs assess your competence (knowledge, skills and abilities) in your job.

By completing your induction and the four Induction Award units that link to the Common Induction Standards, you will be well on the way to completing your NVQ in health and social care.

As you progress from being a new worker to a qualified and experienced worker, your path of learning and qualifications could therefore look something like the diagram on the next page.

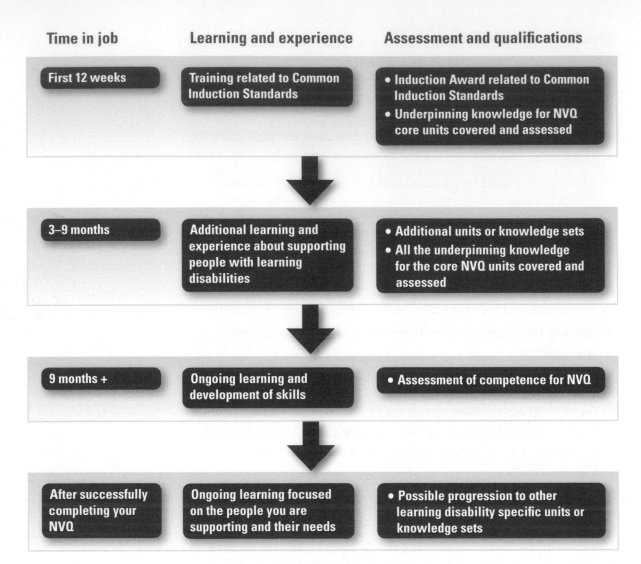

Time in job	Learning and experience	Assessment and qualifications
First 12 weeks	**Training related to Common Induction Standards**	• **Induction Award related to Common Induction Standards** • **Underpinning knowledge for NVQ core units covered and assessed**
3–9 months	**Additional learning and experience about supporting people with learning disabilities**	• **Additional units or knowledge sets** • **All the underpinning knowledge for the core NVQ units covered and assessed**
9 months +	**Ongoing learning and development of skills**	• **Assessment of competence for NVQ**
After successfully completing your NVQ	**Ongoing learning focused on the people you are supporting and their needs**	• **Possible progression to other learning disability specific units or knowledge sets**

▲ A possible path of learning and qualifications for new support workers

Working with people with learning disabilities, family carers and support workers

From day one in your work with people with learning disabilities it is important that you listen carefully to what the people you support are saying to you about their interests, needs and the support you will be providing. In researching and writing this book the author has worked closely with people with learning disabilities and has sought information about people's experiences and their views on what new workers need to know and do. Their contributions are woven throughout this book. The author has also consulted with new and experienced support workers and family carers.

Confidentiality and consent

As you work through the activities in this book, you may wish to include the person you support by, for example, talking with them about their life and using the information in an assignment. It is really important to obtain the consent of the person if you plan to include them in this way. Discuss your organisation's **confidentiality policy** with your line manager if you are unsure what to do.

Language and labels

Ideally we should call people by their name and not label them according to their age, ethnicity, religion, disability, or indeed for any other reason. We should always see the person first and not the labels that others attach to them. However, there are times when labels, no matter how much we may dislike them, are used by all of us and for all of us, for example, students, teenagers, senior citizens, patients, claimants, fans, etc.

It has been discussed for many years how we should describe people with learning disabilities. Over time, the language we use changes because terms come to have new or different meanings or because people object to the labels that are used to describe them. It is important that we are sensitive to people's concerns about the labels that others might use to describe them.

Throughout this book the terms 'people with a learning disability' or 'people with learning disabilities' are used, as these are the terms most commonly found in health and social care settings. Some organisations, including ones run by people with learning disabilities, prefer the term 'people with learning difficulties', which is also used in schools and colleges. The term 'social care worker' or 'support worker' is generally used for paid members of staff. Those employed directly to provide social care support for people with a learning disability are generally referred to as 'personal assistants'.

The word 'service' is used to refer to the workplace situation, whether this is supported living, day opportunities, community support or residential and nursing care. The word 'organisation' is used to refer to agencies that run services. Other terms that may not be clear are explained as they arise in the text or in the glossary.

How this book is organised

This book is interactive. As well as reading, you will be asked to think about examples of support given to people with learning disabilities, give your own ideas, talk to colleagues and try out some of the activities.

confidentiality
concerning things that need to be kept private

policy
a statement or plan of action that clearly sets out an organisation's position or approach on a particular issue and tells staff what should be done in the circumstances

In the next section you will find **Study skills advice** to help you get the most from the time you spend studying and to ensure that it will be enjoyable and successful.

Each chapter contains the following features.

Learning outcomes. There are eight learning outcomes to the Principles of Learning Disability Support units at levels 2 and 3 of the Induction Award: Supporting People who have a Learning Disability. Each of these learning outcomes is given a chapter in this book.

 Activities provide exercises designed to encourage you to apply what you have learned to your work situation.

 Key points summarise the main ideas in the chapter.

 Thinking points are suggestions for you to reflect on your own experiences and how they may affect the support you provide.

 Scenarios are brief studies illustrating ideas or issues covered in the chapter.

 Policy references give information about the key policies, laws and guidance that directly affect you as a social care worker and that set out what you have to do in your work.

 Examples provide detailed studies illustrating the key ideas covered in the chapter. These are designed to develop your ability to discuss and think more deeply about the topics as you cover them, provide an opportunity to reflect on the type of support you and your colleagues give to the people with learning disabilities you work with and give an overview of how they apply in your work on a day-to-day basis.

At the end of the book you will find the following sections.

Commentaries on the examples provides detailed feedback for each of the examples from the end of each chapter to help you review your work on each once it is completed.

Glossary provides explanations of technical words or phrases used in this book in plain, jargon-free English. These words are also explained in the margins, close to where they first appear in the book.

NVQ mapping provides detailed references showing the links to NVQ health and social care qualifications.

Resources lists the key publications, DVDs and websites to refer to if you want additional information on any of the topics covered in this book.

Study skills advice

We all vary in how we study and learn. Some people prefer to study in short bursts, spreading their learning over a long period. Others prefer more sustained periods of concentration. Some of us like to study early in the day and others don't start until late in the evening. No one way of working is better than another. You should find a way that suits you. The following guidelines will help you to get the most from the time you spend studying and help to ensure that it will be enjoyable and successful.

The right environment

You will study better in a quiet room that is free from distractions and where you will be undisturbed. Make sure that your seat is comfortable and supportive and that you have enough working space to spread out your study materials. Good lighting will make reading easier and help prevent your eyes from getting tired.

Identifying and using resources

You may find some of the topics covered in this book interest you so much that you want to find out further information about them. You can find information about working with people with learning disabilities from:

- books
- newspapers
- magazines
- journals
- websites
- television
- colleagues
- people with learning disabilities.

It's a good idea to keep a record of your resources. You could cut out and keep newspaper or magazine articles and make a note of websites you have visited or television programmes you have watched. You will need to have a good filing system so that you can organise these resources to enable you to find what you need quickly.

Reading

We read for many different reasons and purposes. The reading you do for your studies is likely to be very different from reading for leisure. Probably the most important difference is the way you work through the text. When you read a novel, you will usually open it at the first page and read through to the end. This is known as 'passive reading' because you are reading everything without question. When you are studying, you may read only one chapter, or use the index to find information on one subject that is located in various places through the book. This is known as 'active reading' because you are finding the answer to a question.

When you are studying, it's a good idea to give yourself targets so that you read more effectively. You could ask yourself questions such as:

- Do I really need to know this information?
- Do I need to know some of this information?
- Is this nothing at all to do with what I need to know?

As you go through the text, have a pen near you to take notes, or a highlighter or Post-its to mark key points. This will help you to sift out information which will be useful to you.

Reading styles

Once you have established the purpose of your reading you can identify the style of reading most suited to your task. The most commonly used types of reading are:

- **Skimming** involves going through a text quickly at about two to three times your normal reading speed. Look at the index, chapter headings, introduction and conclusion, as well as looking at the first line of each paragraph. This is a useful technique for deciding whether the book contains any information that is useful to you.
- **Scanning** is useful when you know exactly what you are looking for, such as a telephone number or place name. You find the word or phrase you are looking for and then follow the text.
- **Search reading** is used to look for key words and phrases which will help you find specific information. Look in the index to see where you will find key words and topics. Then locate these in the publication by scanning though until you find the words or phrases you are interested in.
- **Receptive reading** is where you need to have a good general understanding or to find out accurately what has been written. When reading receptively you need time to pay close attention to the text, think about what you have read and perhaps make notes.

Taking notes

One of the most important skills to develop through your studies is the ability to make clear and concise notes. You can make notes in training sessions or as you read a book or article or watch a television programme. Making notes helps you to understand a topic and identify its key points.

A common mistake when taking notes is to write everything down. You can make more useful notes by thinking about what you are looking for before you start reading the material or listening to the presentation. Produce notes that are relevant only to what you are looking for and try not to be sidetracked by writing down information you don't need.

There are different ways of taking notes. You should choose a method that suits you. Bear in mind that you will have to remember what they mean later on. Some ways of taking notes are:

- a short summary of the main points
- numbered points or structured lists
- a list of headings and subheadings
- mind maps, patterns and spider diagrams
- shorthand
- key points.

You should write down where you have taken your notes from, for example, the publication or the website. If you use the information in an assignment you will need to say where you got it from. This is known as *referencing*. Use highlighter pens where you can to highlight the main points. Post-it notes are useful to mark important information that you can return to later on.

Organising your time

Spending time planning your studies can be helpful. Firstly, you can avoid a last-minute rush to meet deadlines. Secondly, if you plan how you are going to approach each task you are more likely to carry out each stage effectively and produce a higher quality piece of work. The key stages of organising your time effectively are:

- **Being realistic** is important if you want to organise your time effectively. To work out how much time you actually have to study each week you should ask yourself what other commitments you have that take up time, such as:
  - work
  - family
  - social events

- **Planning ahead** is essential. You will need to ask yourself a number of questions:
  - What exactly is involved?
  - How long will it take?
  - When will you do it?
  - How will you do it?
  - What is the deadline for completion?

- **Organising your studies** carefully will enable you to make the best use of the time you have available and help you to stay motivated and on track. Break large tasks down into manageable chunks:
  - Plan a timetable of when you will do each task.
  - Remember that it might be useful to allocate a larger amount of time to some activities. For example, writing an assignment may be better done in one session so that your ideas flow more easily.
  - Prioritise – don't do the easiest thing first, but the most immediate thing first.

Being flexible

The unexpected always happens, so don't become upset or disheartened if you are unable to stick to your timetable. Ask yourself what needs to be done to get back on track and don't be afraid to ask colleagues, family and friends to support you.

Confidentiality and consent

This book encourages you to relate what you are learning to your work situation. As part of this you will need to reflect on the way you work with people with learning disabilities. Before you involve an individual with learning disabilities in any activities from the book you will need to obtain their consent. Discuss this with your line manager before going ahead.

If you use information about or observations of your colleagues or individuals with learning disabilities in your written work you should be aware of the need for confidentiality. Rather than use someone's real name, you should use a false name or an initial to identify them. You should show the individuals what you have written or tell them about it to check that they are comfortable with what you have written. Discuss your organisation's confidentiality policy with your line manager before completing any of the activities.

Plagiarism

Passing off someone else's work as your own or using someone else's work without acknowledging them is a form of cheating known as plagiarism. Copying other people's work is a serious matter and it is not acceptable to pass off someone else's ideas as your own when you are completing any written work, such as an assignment.

Plagiarism includes:

- copying directly from a book, website, handout or another learner's work
- unfairly using another person's ideas in your work or rewriting a passage from a book or website without saying where you got the ideas from.

You can read books, handouts and information from the Internet when you are studying. To make sure you are not accused of plagiarism when writing an assignment you should always:

- complete it in your own words
- make sure, if you are studying with other people, that you each produce a different assignment
- use quotation marks if you quote directly from someone else's work – for example, 'prejudice means that we have preconceived opinions that are not based on reason'
- acknowledge fully where you obtained your information if you want to quote from a book or article or information you have obtained from the Internet – for example, give the title, author and date of publication and the publisher (for example, see page 90)
- include the web address and the date you obtained the information if you use ideas from a website.

Using the Internet

The Internet contains a wealth of information to help you with your studies. Most of it is extremely valuable. However, some websites contain information that is not reliable. Here are some things to bear in mind when using the Internet for research.

Use only websites that you know to contain reliable information. For example, if you were researching government policies you would go to an official government website. If you wanted information about a particular learning disability you would find it on the website of an organisation that supports people who have that learning disability.

Remember to note down the website address to show where you obtained the information. Do not copy information directly from a website into your own written work without saying where you got it from, as this would be a form of plagiarism.

Do not buy ready-made assignments from the Internet. This is also plagiarism.

Promoting person-centred values

1

> 'Respect is important to me. People should take you as you are, and you should do the same to them.'
>
> Elaine, *Self-advocate*

Introduction

We all have our own values that have developed as a result of our family and childhood experiences, and as a result of our friendships and relationships. Our values are also influenced by people in our local community, as well as by national figures and the media. Support workers in social care are expected to promote particular values.

There are two important points to note. First, the idea that learning disability workers are *supporting* a person. It is not a question of being in charge or in control, because choice and decision-making should lie with the person, as far as possible. Second, it is very important that these principles are part of your *everyday* work. There should be nothing special about them, they should be part of day-to-day life.

Learning outcomes

This chapter will:

- explain the need to promote person-centred values, and what each of the following terms means when supporting people who have a learning disability:
    - individuality
    - rights
    - choice
    - privacy
    - independence
    - dignity
    - respect
    - partnership
    - equal opportunities

- give examples of ways to put these values into practice in your day-to-day support of people with a learning disability

- explain why it is important to work in a way that promotes these values.

Understanding values

First we need to explore what each of the following terms means in practice in your everyday work when supporting people who have learning disabilities. As you go through these explanations, notice how these values do not stand alone, for example, choice and independence and respect, individuality and dignity are closely related to each other. You can think of these values as a network of support for a person with a learning disability.

Thinking point

If you had to describe yourself to other people, what would you say? What are your hopes, dreams, interests and needs?

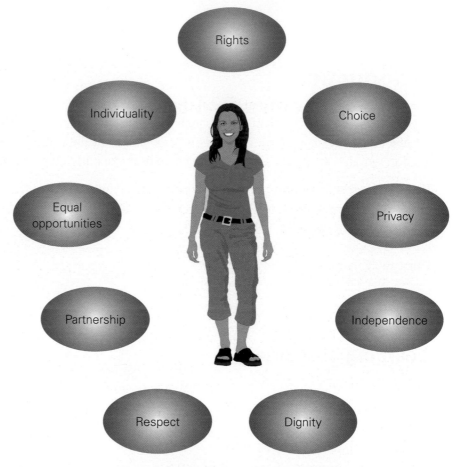

▲ These are the key values that support workers should promote in working with people who have a learning disability.

Key point

Individuality in the work context means that you see each person as an individual and promote their interests, aspirations and needs in all you do.

Individuality

Within a few days of starting work with people with learning disabilities, it should be clear to you that everyone you work with is an individual, with their own particular likes, dislikes, strengths and personality. **Services** and support workers should always focus on the individuals they are working with, rather than the needs of a group of people. You and your colleagues should have the hopes, dreams, interests and needs of each person you support as a top priority in your daily work.

services

provision of social care support for a person in their own home or elsewhere

Rights

As citizens, the **rights** of people with learning disabilities are protected by law, and in particular by the Human Rights Act 1998. Most people with learning disabilities who are supported by health and social care organisations are protected by the rights included in this Act. Sixteen basic human rights have been incorporated into UK law. These rights protect everyone from harm, and set out what we can say and do, as well as our right to a fair trial and other basic entitlements.

rights
a framework of laws that protects people from harm and guarantees them basic entitlements such as the right to respect, equality and fair trial

Human Rights Act 1998

1. The right to life
2. Prohibition of torture
3. Prohibition of slavery and forced labour
4. The right to liberty and security
5. The right to a fair trial
6. No punishment without law
7. The right to respect for private and family life
8. Freedom of thought, conscience and religion
9. Freedom of expression
10. Freedom of assembly and association
11. The right to marry
12. Prohibition of discrimination
13. Protection of property
14. Right to education
15. Right to free elections
16. Abolition of the dealth penalty

In addition to the Human Rights Act, there are a number of laws that have been put in place to protect all of us. They are there to ensure we are treated fairly and not discriminated against, for example because of our sex, race or because we have a disability.

advocacy
speaking up for yourself or someone else

In 2004, an **advocacy** organisation called the Bournemouth Forum Independent Speaking-Up Group did some research. They reported that people with learning disabilities say the following rights are particularly important to them:

'the right to live where you want to live'

'the right to have feelings'

'the right to say no'

'the right to independence'

'the right to feel safe when going out'

'the right to adulthood'

'the right to relationships'

'the right to transportation'

'the right to feel safe in our own homes'

'the right to confidentiality'

Policy reference

Sex Discrimination Act 1975 (amended 1986)

Race Relations Act 1976 (amended 2000)

Disability Discrimination Act 1995

Scenario: The right to feel safe in their own homes

Many individuals with disabilities have little or no choice about where they live, or who they live with. The investigation by the Healthcare Commission (2006) into services for people with learning disabilities provided by Sutton and Merton Primary Care Trust found that residents of one care home regularly shared their home with individuals receiving respite care. It was found some of these individuals behaved aggressively towards the residents. Imagine how you would feel if people who you had not invited, and who frightened you, regularly came to stay in your home.

You have an important role in upholding people's rights and in showing others in the community how to support people with learning disabilities.

There are short, clear guides available on the UN Declaration on Human Rights and the Human Rights Act. These are the rights of everyone with a learning disability, because they are the rights of every human being. They are your basic rights too, and the rights of your family and friends. Get to know them, and you will find that they will help you, not only as a guide in many areas of your work, but also in your own life.

Choice

Every day we make many choices. All choices are important, even though some of them are quite small. Some can be more far-reaching. Day-to-day choices are often about the clothes we wear, the food we eat, how we spend our money and who we spend time with. Other choices we make include where to work, who to live with, where to live and where to go on holiday. You probably take the freedom to make these choices for granted, but these choices are often made for people with learning disabilities, without paying attention to their wishes.

Choice is not only for people who can speak for themselves. People with severe or profound learning disabilities can make many choices for themselves. You will need to develop your observation skills to discover the ways in which the person you support expresses their preferences. Over time you will be able to build up a more detailed understanding of how they communicate their likes and dislikes. You can then use this information to involve the person in making more choices.

Having choice over a particular part of your life means you have control. This is good for your emotional and mental health, and helps you feel a real part of the community. Part of your task is ensuring that people with learning difficulties have choice in their lives.

Privacy

Privacy is a basic human need. We all need to do some things alone and to have time to ourselves to do as we please. Our need for privacy depends on our personality, interests and circumstances. You must respect people's need for privacy whenever it arises. If your work involves supporting a person with their personal care, you will need to make particular efforts to ensure privacy for them.

Key point
Choice means having access to a wide range of options and information. People need to know the pros and cons of all the options to decide for themselves which ones suit them best.

Thinking point
What does privacy mean for you? Would you describe yourself as someone who needs a lot of privacy? Where do you go when you want time to yourself?

Key point
We respect peoples' privacy by ensuring that their dignity is safeguarded, and by protecting them from situations that might cause them distress.

▲ We all need a quiet space of our own.

Independence

None of us is truly independent, however much we may wish to be. We are dependent on other people for all aspects of our daily life. Think about the supply of electricity and water to our homes, the food we eat and the transport we use, not to mention access to communication technology such as phones, TV and the Internet. More importantly, we are dependent on those close to us for their love, support and affection. It is more accurate to say that we are all interdependent. We need other people in all areas of our life. There are, however, different types of independence. You can see this with children, as they grow from being totally dependent babies to much more independent teenagers.

Gradually, people with learning disabilities are taking more control of their lives. But even today, people with learning disabilities are often on the receiving end of other people's decisions and planning. They may not have the power to decide their own lifestyle. Other people, such as service providers, families or support workers, often make these decisions for them. Others may be well supported, but lack the confidence or experience to take control of their lives. You have a vitally important role in the **empowerment** of people with learning disabilities to become independent.

Dignity

People with learning disabilities have the same rights as every other citizen in our society. This fundamental principle means that people with learning disabilities should never be treated in an inhuman or degrading way. They should always be treated politely, and as people of value in their own right. You should always aim to maintain the dignity of each person you work with. Occasionally, this may mean discouraging a person from doing something that would cause them embarrassment or humiliation. By showing dignity in your everyday actions you can reinforce this idea for the person concerned, and for others who see how you support them.

Respect

The way that you and your colleagues behave towards the people with learning disabilities you support affects the way that other people see them, and the way they see themselves. You should always show consideration to the people with learning disabilities that you work with. Your actions and attitudes should show that everyone is worthy of respect.

Activity 1a

Supporting Katie with the shopping

Katie is a young woman with learning disabilities. Imagine you are supporting her on a shopping trip to the local supermarket. Katie begins to feel unwell and becomes distressed, crying loudly and refusing to move. What action would you take to manage the situation, while at the same time treating Katie with dignity and respect? Discuss your answer with your colleagues.

Key point

Respect means behaving towards people with the consideration they deserve, showing that you value their opinions, views and achievements, and taking greater care to be as aware as possible of what the person feels and understands.

Partnership

Every day in your work as a learning disability worker, you are a partner with the person with a learning disability you support. You are working with them so that they can fulfil their dreams and ambitions, and so that you can assist them with their particular needs.

Partnership also involves other people working together, to meet the needs of people with learning disabilities as fully as possible. This may include partnership with other professionals such as social workers, GPs, psychologists, psychiatrists, and speech and language therapists.

The family of the people with learning disabilities you support are often very important partners in your work. Most family carers have a wealth of knowledge and experience about their family member. They know their likes and dislikes, their personal history and any particular medical needs. They are often more than happy to share what they know with new workers.

When asking family carers for information, it is important to remember that some families have seen many workers come and go in their relative's life. They may have repeated the same information very many times. Some may feel disillusioned because of past experiences, when things have not changed as they had hoped.

'We're John's family, so of course we care about him and how he's getting on when he's not with us. Over the years there's been loads of paid people in his life. We get on best with the ones who want to work with us to support him. When it's a partnership we feel more relaxed about his life with them.'

Amanda, Family carer

▲ Relatives can be important partners in your work.

A major aspect of partnership working is bringing people together in an atmosphere where this is simply the accepted way of doing things. In this type of working environment, training, attitudes, procedures and quality standards all have partnership as one of their goals. Successful partnerships depend to a large extent upon the amount of effort put into creating an environment in which joint working is seen simply as the way things are done.

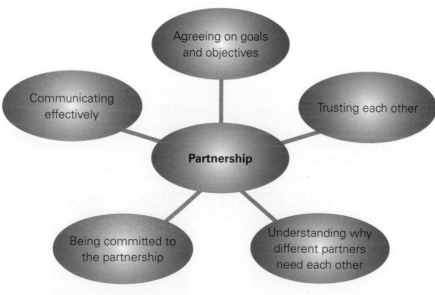

▲ Important aspects of partnership

Equal opportunities

Discrimination against people with learning disabilities and their families often results in the unfair and unequal treatment of people just because of their learning disability. People with learning disabilities may not be allowed the freedom and opportunities which the Human Rights Act and other laws encourage. They often face **prejudice** and discrimination. They may be treated unequally and unjustly and denied the opportunities that should be available to them, just as they are to other citizens.

Equal opportunities mean that people with learning disabilities should:

- no longer be marginalised and isolated within society
- have the same social status as other people
- no longer be subject to exploitation and abuse
- have their opinions taken seriously
- have their adult status recognised
- have the same citizenship rights as other people.

Failure to give equal opportunities to people with learning disabilities denies our common humanity. It causes anger, frustration, despair, helplessness and loneliness for the people involved, and keeps them powerless and dependent.

The **General Social Care Council (GSCC)** is the organisation set up by the government in 2001 to register and regulate all social care workers. It has produced a **_Code of Practice_** which states that social care workers should work in a certain way. You can see some of these requirements in the table below:

Code of Practice for Social Care Workers requirements
Protect the rights and promote the interests of service users and carers
Strive to establish and maintain the trust and confidence of service users and carers
Promote the independence of service users, while protecting them as far as possible from danger or harm
Respect the rights of service users, while seeking to ensure that their behaviour does not harm themselves or other people

Working with the values we have just discussed will help you to fulfil these requirements.

prejudice
negative value judgements or opinions about someone

Thinking point
What do you think equal opportunities means for a person you know who has a learning disability?

General Social Care Council
the organisation that regulates the social care workforce in England and sets the standard of care through the Codes of Practice

Code of Practice
a UK document for social care workers setting out the standards they should work to

Policy reference
General Social Care Council _Code of Practice for Social Care Workers_ (2002)

General Social Care Council _Code of Practice for Employers of Social Care Workers_ (2002)

Why it is important to promote rights and values

When we talk about promoting rights and values, we mean:

- actively using those rights and values to influence everything we do
- seeing them as having an important role in all our work as learning disability workers
- encouraging their use as the standards by which we and others judge the quality of life of the people we support, and the quality of the services that support them.

This is a big task. The use of values as standards is a huge challenge to services. But the idea is central to the basic principles of supporting people with learning disabilities.

To demonstrate that you have understood this, you should be able to discuss why it is important to work in a way that promotes these values when supporting those who have a learning disability. The following example should help you to develop the skills you will need to discuss values in relation to the lives of the people you support.

Example 1: Promoting key values

Emma is a young woman in her twenties, who has learning disabilities. Following the death of her mother, who has been her main carer, Emma has been given a place in a residential home. This is a bungalow in a suburban area much sought after by retired people. The place became vacant when a previous resident died. The other two women are 40 years older than Emma, and were close friends of the woman she has replaced.

Emma uses a basic wheelchair. She is not strong enough to move the chair more than short distances by herself, but she has difficulty using a powered chair. The bungalow and transport available are not suitable. The support workers have complained about the problems she causes because of her need for extra support for mobility in and out of the home.

continued ▶

The workers at the home have found it difficult to assess Emma's communication abilities. This is partly due to delays in obtaining speech and language therapy support, but mainly because she is very slow to speak. Most day-to-day communication is through signing. Support workers have reported that Emma's attention span is short and that she can be irritable, and even aggressive.

Emma's father is in a residential home for the elderly because he is unable to care for himself. He does not visit his daughter often because her two fellow residents do not like him. Because of her speech difficulties and problems with transport, Emma has problems keeping in touch by phone or visits.

Emma is described as vain about her appearance. Getting her to accept clothes to wear at the beginning of the day has been described as a nightmare. When she lived at home with her parents she had visits for an afternoon every week from two young student beauty therapists. The two young women would do her hair, give her a manicure, help her with make-up and even take her shopping for clothes. Sometimes they would take her into their college.

The home manager has stopped the trips for safety reasons. He has discouraged the students' visits and shortened them because the chatter and laughter disturbs the other two women. Emma now has her hair done by the woman who has looked after the other residents for twenty years. Her nails are clipped by staff when necessary.

The local citizen advocacy co-ordinator has now contacted the manager to say that it has been suggested that Emma might like to discuss advocacy to find out what it is, and what it might offer her. Policy in the residential service is to encourage advocacy where it is not disruptive. One of the support workers suspects the two college students of stirring things up. But they feel they could do with another pair of hands, provided all advocacy activities are under their supervision and control.

1. Read the example again and, as you read it, think about the values and rights you have been reading about. Note down where you think the support workers and the service they work for have been good at promoting Emma's rights, and where you think they are not promoting the values and rights you have read about.
2. Note down the values you think are particularly important to Emma.
3. Talk to your line manager, or a more experienced colleague, about how you and your service might support Emma in a way that positively promotes the values and rights covered in this chapter.

Now turn to the commentary on this example on page 80.

2

Respecting diversity, cultures and values

'It's good that staff help us to organise evenings out for St Patrick's Day and Diwali. We wouldn't go, otherwise. Wouldn't do anything special.'

Amarjit, *Self-advocate*

Introduction

As a learning disability worker, you must actively support the values of respect, individuality and personal choice. In order to do this well, and in a person-centred way, you will need to understand more about the person you work with, their background and values. Understanding and respecting people's background, and how it can influence the support you provide, is about respecting diversity. It is important to understand that without active support, many expressions of diversity, such as marking special days of celebration, will simply fade away.

Learning outcomes

This chapter will help you to:

- understand why it is important for you to respect all the people you work with, and how you can support each person, taking into account their cultural background and values
- explore examples of aspects of everyday life that might be approached differently by people from different backgrounds
- explain why it is important to support people in ways that respect these differences
- explain practical ways to show respect.

Understanding diversity, cultures and values

For each of us, our identity consists of several important elements, such as our age, gender, class, ethnicity, language and religion. The importance of each element varies from person to person. Identity is important to all of us. It affects the image we have of ourselves, other people's perception of us and how we see our role in society. As a support worker, understanding some of the key aspects that influence a person's identity will help you to support them better.

▲ Britain is a multicultural country – diversity should be valued and respected.

Ethnicity

Ethnicity, or our national, racial, religious, linguistic or cultural origins, is an important element of our identity. Note the use of the plural for 'origins'. As you learned at school, throughout history, many different peoples have settled in this country. Even looking at their recent family history, many people have more than one ethnic background. If we were to go further back in time, we might be surprised at the mix of people who are our ancestors.

As children grow and develop within their own culture, they learn what is normal within that culture. They learn its view on female and male roles, its language and accents, family structures, values, beliefs and priorities, and other elements of identity.

As UK society has become more multiracial, there has been a greater understanding of the importance of ethnic background as part of a person's identity. For example, until fairly recently it was acceptable for black children to be placed in white families for adoption, with little consideration of the child's ethnic background. This is no longer acceptable, and children are more likely to be placed with a family that has a similar racial background to them. Asian immigrants in the 1950s and 1960s were expected to adapt to the dominant white culture when they settled in the UK. Today, society's views are more complex. We promote what it is to be British, as well as celebrating ethnic **diversity**.

diversity
differences in ethnicity, religion, sex and culture

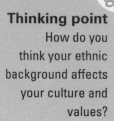

Thinking point
How do you think your ethnic background affects your culture and values?

Although there are still many issues to be resolved, we are at least talking openly now about the importance of ethnicity. This is important in learning disability services as well, not only to people with learning disabilities and their families and friends, but also to staff working to support them.

Religion

Another key element of identity is religion. This can be either belonging to a particular faith or it can be an absence of faith, such as in the case of humanists, atheists and so on. For some people their faith or philosophical system is the basis of their values, beliefs and priorities. It provides them with guidelines for all areas of their lives, and influences their interactions with, and responses to, other people.

As a professional care worker, you must be sensitive to the diversity of views regarding religion that can be found among those we support. This also applies to their friends and families, as well as to our own colleagues. We also have a responsibility to find out about the religious views of the people we support.

Language

Children are born with a strong capacity for language. Unless their hearing has been damaged, they learn the words of the language they hear around them.

Language and accent are strongly embedded in us. We usually feel more comfortable with people who speak our own language, and who have similar accents to our own. Children sometimes make fun of others who have different accents, such as those they see as 'posh' or 'common', depending on their own 'class' (see page 17).

Understanding other differences

Ethnicity, religion and language are important elements of who we are, but there are a number of other factors that make up an individual's identity. If you bear these in mind, they will help you to improve the quality of support you give to people.

Age

Age is very important to young children. Birthdays, for example, are exciting events, with all the thrill of being the centre of attention and moving on to new experiences. The number itself may not mean much to them, but they know that the world holds more freedom and opportunities as they get older. They are very aware of their own limitations in relation to grown-ups. They act out adult roles in their play.

▲ Find out what is important to people and help them to celebrate.

Age continues to play an important part in our identity as we get older. But it is the subjective aspects (that is, society's attitudes and perceptions), rather than the number of years we have lived, that gradually take over. In UK society, improvements in health and increasing wealth mean that people are living longer. This, in turn, influences the way we think of age.

People who retire at 60 or 65 no longer think of themselves as elderly. Indeed, they may not see themselves as retired, but as people who have taken advantage of their pensions to live new lifestyles without the interference of work. Expectations of people of this age have changed dramatically. It was not long ago that people of 70 were seen as very old; now we are quite surprised if they are not physically and mentally active.

Attitudes and perceptions are also influenced by the age of those involved and their comparative age differences. To an 18-year-old, 60 is very old indeed. A 55-year-old takes a somewhat different view, and so does a 90-year-old.

Gender

Children learn from an early age whether they are boys or girls. But they also learn about gender, which is not the same as sex. Sex determines whether we are male or female. Gender is more to do with how society views men and women. This means that the society in which we live determines which roles are appropriate for men, and which for women.

Gender is a very complex concept, and one about which there are many disagreements. This is why it remains an important element of identity and diversity.

Gender roles change over time. This was particularly true in western society during the twentieth century. For example, there were big changes in areas such as women going out to work, earning equal pay, voting, driving and doing certain jobs such as engineering or soldiering. This has an additional age-related effect. Older people will remember these changes. Younger people may not really be aware that they have happened, although issues such as equal pay remain.

Perceptions of gender also differ from culture to culture, and from class to class. The roles and expectations of men and women in British culture differ from those in some other cultures. The roles and expectations of men and women may also vary, say, between northern manufacturing and ex-mining communities, and upper class families in the rural counties of middle England.

In some countries of the Middle East women are still not allowed to drive or vote, do not receive a full education, and may have limited economic roles. There are parts of Latin America where the concept of *machismo* leads men to behave in ways towards each other and towards women which are very different from those we are used to. Children learn about gender from observing how men and women function and relate to one another, particularly in their own culture.

Nowadays, children and others are also strongly influenced by the ways in which gender roles are played out in television, computer games and films.

Scenario: Traditional roles

Adam is 22 years old, and has lived with his parents all his life. When he moves into supported living accommodation with two other people, they soon become annoyed because Adam refuses to help with the housework and cooking. When the support worker talks to Adam about it, he finds that Adam comes from a 'traditional' family. His mother stayed at home to look after the children and house, and his father went to work. Adam, like his father, was not expected to help around the house. It is not surprising then that Adam doesn't offer to help in his new home. His support worker and new housemates work hard with Adam over the following months to help him think about new roles and ways of doing things.

Class

Class is another important element in Britain. Class is a shorthand term for describing the complex structures that exist in our society. We associate certain characteristics with certain groups that we call classes. These often include type of education, accent, dress, place and type of home, job and lifestyle. In addition, there are the two key factors of birth and money.

Other countries and cultures have different ways of classifying people within society. They may classify people through their lifestyle, social mobility, type of education, religious status, or personal achievements. Some of these attitudes have been brought to this country by various cultural and religious groups. Among Hindus, for example, it is still a widely-held belief that you are born into your position in life and should remain there. Americans, on the other hand, have their dream that if the poorest child born there works hard, they could rise to be President.

Key point

Everyone you come into contact with in your work as a learning disability worker deserves respect. Finding out about a person's background will help you to understand their values and beliefs, and to provide the right support.

The need to respect and support differences

There may well be people with learning disabilities who you support who are from different backgrounds from your own. This means that they and their families may also have a different understanding of care and support services. For example, you might work with people whose cultural backgrounds lead them to:

- live very closely with extended family members
- have lots more people in their family
- have different expectations of the role of men and women
- have arranged marriages
- have different ideas of what ability and disability mean
- expect sons and daughters to live with the family until marriage
- expect sons and daughters to live with the family until they leave home, regardless of their age
- have important religious requirements
- have particular dietary or dress requirements.

Activity 2a

Finding out about cultural backgrounds

Think about how you could find out about the cultural background of a new person you are supporting. How could you find out about their values and beliefs? Discuss your ideas with your line manager or a senior colleague.

Diversity and people with learning disabilities

Cultural groups and identity are just as important to people with learning disabilities as they are to the rest of us. In fact, because they may have disadvantages in other areas of life, the status and sense of identity that comes from belonging to a cultural group may be even more important to them than to most people. There are a number of reasons why it is important to support people with learning disabilities in ways which respect differences.

Prejudice and discrimination

Prejudice is a negative value judgement or opinion that is harmful to the person involved. It is usually based on a lack of knowledge and awareness. Prejudice influences the way that people with learning disabilities are treated in society, and leads to discrimination.

People with learning disabilities already experience discrimination in many walks of life, such as:

- education
- employment
- housing
- public places and institutions
- leisure and recreational activities
- mainstream services or support.

There may be additional discrimination if an individual also belongs to a particular cultural group or groups. Two factors in particular can cause this: ethnicity and gender.

Racial discrimination and people with learning disabilities

People from different ethnic groups often experience racial discrimination, as well as discrimination because of their learning disabilities. The government White Paper *Valuing People* recognises that 'People with learning disabilities from minority ethnic communities and their families are too often overlooked… Social exclusion is made more severe by language barriers and racism, and negative stereotypes and attitudes contribute to disadvantage… Agencies often underestimate people's attachment to cultural traditions and religious beliefs.'

Sex discrimination and people with learning disabilities

Women with learning disabilities are often even more oppressed than men with learning disabilities. Here are some examples:

- Even in the self-advocacy movement, gender bias is common. For example, men usually hold the most influential roles. They are the ones whose voices are most often heard.
- Gender issues are seldom looked at in debates and policy discussions about people with learning disabilities.

Thinking point

Everyone has some prejudices, no matter how small. Be honest and think about your own prejudices, and how they might affect the way you provide support to someone from a different background.

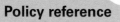

Policy reference

Department of Health (2001) *Valuing People: A New Strategy for Learning Disability for the 21st Century*

- Women with learning disabilities are often considered not to be believable witnesses in cases of sexual abuse.
- Many doubt the parenting skills of mothers with a learning disability.

▲ People with learning disabilities may need support to do the same things as everyone else, but they should not be discriminated against.

Multiple discrimination

Multiple discrimination is where people are **discriminated** against for several reasons. These include some or all of the following:

> **discriminated**
> *treated unfairly, often because of a person's race, religion or sex*

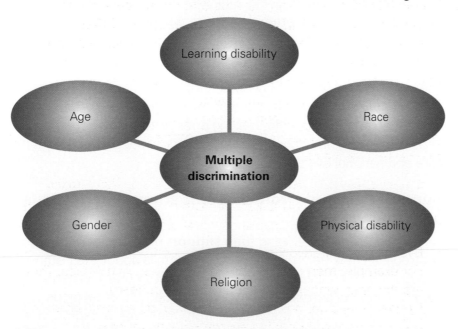

▲ Two or more of these reasons lead to multiple discrimination.

Multiple discrimination is cumulative. This means that each type of discrimination experience adds to the effects of the other, and leads to further discrimination. For example, a woman might be discriminated against because of her gender, but also because she is Asian and has Down's syndrome. A man might encounter prejudice because he has a learning disability, is elderly and is from an Afro-Caribbean background.

Respecting diversity in practical ways

How can you respect the diversity of people with learning disabilities? To begin with, all support workers have a responsibility to:

- work in ways that value every person
- recognise and support racial identity
- take full account of gender issues in our work
- take account of age issues
- deal with any discriminatory practices in the workplace and community.

The best way of helping people with learning disabilities to avoid discrimination and prejudice is to help them become empowered through:

- developing a strong belief in themselves
- knowing their rights
- gaining the confidence to challenge discrimination.

The extent to which individuals are able to do this can depend on the degree of their learning disability. It also depends on their circumstances and opportunities. There will always be people who need others to advocate for them and fight for their rights. But the principle is the same.

There are many practical ways that support workers and organisations can show people that their cultures and values are respected. For example, making arrangements to support important practices relating to food, religious practices, personal care and national events and celebrations.

Supporting people from different ethnic and religious backgrounds

When people are developing their **support plan** and their person-centred plan, it is helpful if they include details about their ethnic background and religion if they are important to them. When a service supports someone from a different ethnic or religious background it is helpful if someone from the same background is involved to ensure that the person gets the support they need.

Miriam's support plan
Religious life

I like to go to the synagogue.

When I go to the synagogue I need to wear something to cover my head.

These are some important dates when I would like to go to the synagogue in 2007 and 2008.

13 and 14 September
Rosh Hashanah (Jewish New Year)

5–13 December
Hanukkah (Festival of Lights)

21 March
Purim (Festival of Lots)

▲ A page from Miriam's support plan

For example, Miriam comes from a Jewish background and visits the synagogue several times a year for important festivals and holy days. None of the support workers supporting Miriam is Jewish so she asks her older brother to come and explain to the staff about the importance for her of going to the synagogue.

Challenging racism, ageism and sexism

Incidents of racism, ageism and sexism should be challenged and managed appropriately by all the support workers in an organisation. For example, when Max was going swimming with Doug at the local pool, he heard a new attendant say to Doug that he was 'a silly old fool'. Max spoke to the attendant and his supervisor to challenge what he said. Now every time Max and Doug go swimming they talk to the attendant so that he gets to know them better.

▲ Incidents of racism, ageism and sexism should be challenged.

Activity 2b

Practical ways to show respect

Write down three practical ways that you and the organisation you work for can show respect for a person's culture and values. Discuss your ideas with your line manager.

As you can see, it is important to get into the habit of thinking about how you can promote diversity and support different cultures and values in your work. The following example, from a discussion with people with learning disabilities who live actively in their local community, will give you more ideas to think about.

Example 2: Respecting diversity, cultures and values

There were people in the group who had family backgrounds in India, Ireland and the Caribbean. There were men and women. There was a mix of characters: lively, quiet, chatty, humorous, serious, etc. Some people liked each other, and some did not.

Not surprisingly, given how different each person was, everyone felt that difference and diversity should be treated with respect. 'People should take you as you are, and you should do the same to them.'

*Each person had photo albums, **life story books** and other records. The pictures in these showed the different backgrounds, families and cultures they each came from. They were able to use these books to show new people they met the things that were important and valued in their lives.*

People in the group were polite when talking about different cultures. Some of them liked foods from each others' cultures. The support workers helped organise something special for events with special meaning to different people, such as St Patrick's Day, Christmas and Diwali. These occasions often involved a special meal, or an evening out, and were obviously enjoyed by everyone. Support workers also discussed the different backgrounds people came from, including members of staff themselves.

There was a feeling that, while it was good to lead your own life, it was also a pleasure sometimes to join in activities with others.

1. This is an example of how diversity can be celebrated with success. Consider what the outcome might be for the people concerned if this was not the case. You might be able to provide examples from your own experience. Make brief notes of these.

2. Valuing and respecting diversity are only important if they have an impact on the person's life. Identify three practical ways mentioned in the example in which the people with learning disabilities and the support workers show people that their differences were respected.

3. From your own work experience, suggest two more practical ways that you could use to respond positively to people from a different background to your own.

Now turn to the commentary on this example on page 81.

life story book
an account of a person's life, including stories and memories of past events, relationships and experiences that make us who we are

3 Understanding personal history and preferences

'When I didn't know what I wanted at college, I was just left to do the washing-up every day. I went there to learn catering, but I didn't learn anything. Except washing-up!'

Carol, *Self-advocate*

Introduction

It is now widely accepted that the person with learning disabilities should be at the centre of all decision-making that affects their life. Putting the individual's needs and choices at the centre of the care and support you provide is often referred to as using a **person-centred approach** in the way you work.

In order to put the person at the centre of the process of care and support, it is essential to find out about their history, preferences, wishes and needs. You can then use this information to make sure you or others provide high-quality support.

person-centred approach
a way of working every day with people with learning disabilities that puts the person and their dreams at the centre of everything you do

Learning outcomes

In this chapter you will find out:

- why it is important to know about the history and preferences, wishes and needs of the people with learning disabilities you work with
- practical steps you can take to find out more fully about the preferences and history of a person you support.

Why it is important to get to know a person

If you were planning a surprise holiday for a partner or loved one, or a party for a child, you would take account of their interests, likes and dislikes. You wouldn't immediately think about taking someone who was passionate about mountains for a city break in central Europe, or taking a quiet, nervous child for a birthday treat to a busy, noisy theme park. When you are supporting a person with a learning disability it is also important that you find out about their history, preferences, wishes and needs so that you can support them appropriately.

Once you have this information, you can use it to make sure that your support focuses on their skills and achievements, rather than on what they cannot do. As you develop in your role as a support worker, you will learn more about the person and also develop better, more flexible ways of supporting them.

Practical steps to find out someone's wishes

When you start supporting a person with a learning disability, you need to get to know them, and there can be a lot of information to find out.

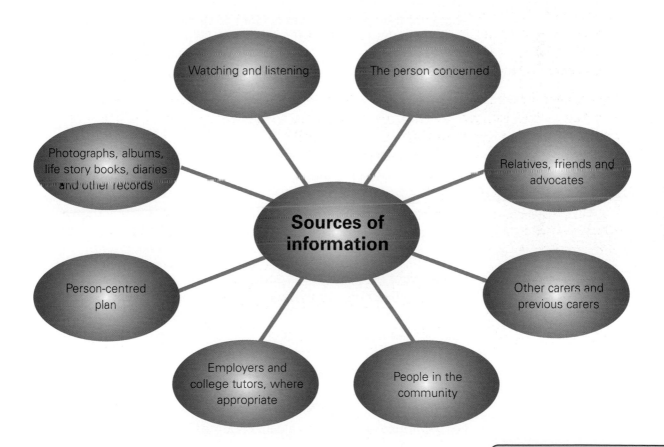

▲ You can find out the information you need from a variety of sources.

When gathering background on a person's history, preferences, wishes and needs, always remember to use appropriate methods of communication. These could include gesture, sign or symbol systems and **total communication**. You should share information with and about the person in positive and supportive ways.

total communication
using the best methods for an individual, always in conjunction with speech, according to how they communicate in various environments

What the person with a learning disability can tell you

You will need to gradually find out from the person you support what they want from life, their dreams for now and the future and what is important to them. So, how do you get this information? The person is the obvious starting point. Even if they cannot communicate in words, this should not prevent you from learning from the person. By being with them in different situations, you can learn a lot about their likes and dislikes, what makes their life meaningful, and the people they like and dislike.

What an advocate can do

advocate
an independent person who supports someone to speak up for themselves

If the person is able to speak up for themselves, they may be able to present their own views and wishes, or they may need some support to do this. When working with people who are unable to speak for themselves you may want to work closely with their **advocate** if they have one. An advocate is independent and will be able to represent the views and wishes of the person. Advocacy is often a very good way for the person to present wishes and choices, express preferences and make informed decisions.

What people who matter most can tell you

The next best sources of information are those who spend most time with the person, care about them and know them best. These are usually family members and friends, perhaps an advocate. They will know a lot about the person, including their past, likes and dislikes and their dreams, and often they are willing to share this information with new support workers.

There might be other useful sources of information, such as the GP or practice nurse, if there are health issues involved. People in the local community, such as a local shopkeeper, community and religious leaders and neighbours may also be able to contribute in particular ways. If the person has a job, talk to the employer. If college courses have been taken, have a word with the tutors concerned. Remember to ask the person's permission before talking to employers or tutors. Sometimes former support workers keep in touch and can be valuable sources on a person's history.

Scenario: Helen's book

Helen is supported by three personal assistants in her own home. She and her family have put together a book containing photographs and information about Helen, her likes and dislikes and how she prefers to be supported. When someone new comes to work with her Helen enjoys going through the book with them.

Key point
The most productive way to find out about a person's wishes is from them. You can also find out information from other people who know them well.

▲ Advocates need to really get to know the people they are supporting.

What you can do

You need to continually listen to and observe the person in everyday situations. People may tell you things about themselves in words, and by their actions. Someone may not tell you they dislike loud music, but when you see them putting their hands over their ears when the radio or CD player is too loud, you have found out something about them by observation. We need to allow some people to tell us things in their own way through their actions, and we need to be skilled observers.

Key point
You should use all means available – listening, observing, conversation – to get to know the dreams and aspirations of the person you are supporting.

Using the information you have gathered

You need to think carefully about what you do with the information you find out about a person. It is also important that you remain open-minded when gathering information. Past history is important, but none of us want the people who know us now to judge us by the negative remarks someone made about us 20 years ago. Would you like your colleagues and friends to be influenced in their relationship with you by the sarcastic or negative comments from a teacher when you were 15? So you need to keep an open mind too. Don't let past history restrict or influence your opinions of a person, or the new opportunities you could offer them. Find out as much as you can, but remember:

- keep an open mind
- people change and grow
- people sometimes get labelled, but the label may be out of date or inaccurate
- the person may have had no opportunity in the past to represent their own interests and point of view.

Sometimes, we can be so enthusiastic to do the right thing, and gather as much information as possible, that we forget that we are dealing with a real person's life. There will be information that is private, sensitive and confidential, and should remain so. Imagine how you would feel if a group of friends wanted to discuss every aspect of your life – how much debt you have, what your relationships are really like, your bad habits – it doesn't bear thinking about!

Your work must therefore always recognise the need for privacy and confidentiality. Not everyone needs to have access to all information. The 'need to know' principle should apply. Sensitive and private information should be made available only to those who need to know, and then only with the permission of the person concerned.

Scenario: All about Amar

Amar is preparing to live independently in his own flat, where he will need several hours of support each day. The following table shows how knowing about Amar's background, interests and choices could affect the way he is supported.

How knowing Amar's background affects the support he is given	
Amar's history and wishes	**Effect on support**
Amar is a vegetarian.	<ul><li>Nutrition, menus, shopping.</li><li>Educate staff in vegetarianism.</li><li>Traditional Indian style foods only? Ask Amar and family.</li></ul>
He comes from a traditional Hindu family.	<ul><li>Check he shares his family's beliefs.</li><li>Religious/spiritual needs? Local temple? Priest?</li><li>Celebration of festivals – as for above. Dates known?</li><li>How can others join in? Meals? Gifts? Greetings?</li><li>Who? Family, staff, friends, visitors.</li></ul>
He supports Aston Villa.	<ul><li>Needs support to get to the match.</li><li>Transport. Home games no problem – but away?</li><li>Safety issues – company policy.</li></ul>

Activity 3

All about someone I support

Think about a person you support and make your own table to reflect on how your knowledge of their likes and dislikes, dreams and preferences influence the support you provide.

Getting to know the person you support is an essential part of being a good support worker. It will enable you to work in a person-centred way. The example below explores how you can get to know someone new when there is little information available about their earlier life and experiences.

Example 3: Exploring personal history and preferences

Jack is in late middle age. No one is quite sure how old he is, or how he came to be in care nearly half a century ago at the age of eight or so. Anyone who might be able to say is dead or has gone away. There are large parts of his personal file which are missing, too, or which were never written up in the first place.

Jack cannot walk, but he uses a wheelchair like an athlete. He cannot speak, but uses a picture board and facial expressions to communicate with great effect. He has a good sense of time and can use a clock. He carries the picture board permanently on the tray of his chair, together with a toy clock and a real travelling clock. It is obvious from his skills and some of his possessions that at times he has had good and caring support.

He was first resettled from a long-stay hospital to temporary accommodation. This was a large Victorian house with 12 residents, most of whom were expected to spend only a few months there, having their daily living skills assessed and improved before moving on to a better and more permanent home. Jack lived there for six years. To everyone's pleasure and surprise he thrived there.

Recently, Jack moved to a well-equipped bungalow in a pleasant suburb. This has been purpose built for people who use wheelchairs and has specially trained staff. The equipment includes special toilet facilities, an adapted kitchen and gardens, as well as dedicated transport, modified to carry wheelchair users. All these points were seen as addressing problems that had been identified in Jack's assessment.

Within a few days of moving to the bungalow, Jack's behaviour became angry and aggressive. There were no previous known or recorded examples of this. The contrast with his typical behaviour was so marked that a psychiatrist was consulted

continued ▶

and the community behavioural support team was brought in. His key worker insisted that he should also be introduced to a citizen advocacy service.

The initial conclusion of the psychiatrist was that any mental health problems Jack had were caused by institutionalisation and were very slight. He suggested efforts be focused on communication. If the behaviour continued, anger management training might be appropriate.

The behavioural support team agreed on the issue of communication. Jack had taken to banging his picture board, apparently in frustration. They also investigated what relevant information was available on his file, to see if anything like this had happened before.

They found that Jack had been one of the last to be resettled from the house. He was seen as someone it would be difficult to introduce to community living, not because of his behaviour, but because he was so deeply institutionalised. Over the years he had become a favourite among the staff, and he was often seen speeding around the building and grounds on errands. By the time he came to leave, he had lost much of this former role, leaving him a somewhat dejected and lonely figure.

Jack's key worker carried out a number of observations at the suggestion of the behavioural support team. These identified two triggers for anger and aggression. The first was that he would make repeated demands, for example for the times of meals, when he knew that he could prepare the food he chose when he chose. He would have this explained to him several times, and would then get angry and throw things. A second trigger seemed to be that his picture board was out of date. He would seem to search for a picture, and on not finding it would get angry.

A volunteer was sent to discuss with Jack whether he would like an advocate. He decided to explore Jack's past with him as a basis for this. Their main resource was a picture album which he had been encouraged to keep by his resettlement team. The volunteer approached this with care, because an earlier attempt to add some photos of the bungalow and the people who lived there and staff had ended with the album's being thrown at the deputy manager.

Because there was so little in the album, the volunteer took some additional photos and showed them to Jack. Among these was one of the Victorian house where he had been assessed. He seized this at once, expressed pleasure, placed it on his picture board, and began pointing at it and then at his symbol for 'Go there'.

1. Imagine you recently started to support Jack. Think about how you would find out about his history, preferences and dreams for the future. How could you get to see the situation from Jack's perspective?

2. What is preventing Jack from expressing his wants? How could you support him to overcome these difficulties?

3. Write down three reasons why you think it is important to find out as much as you can about the person with learning disabilities that you support.

Now turn to the commentary on this example on page 81.

Working in a person-centred way

'I like the way things are all kept personal and about me. Like my health plan is about me, how I feel and what I think and want.'

Annie, *Self-advocate*

Introduction

Many people with learning disabilities need support so that they can have control of their own lives, and take a full part in their community as equal citizens. In supporting people we have discovered that our support is most effective if we work in a person-centred way. Making the person's support fit their dreams, interests and needs gives them control, and it also improves the community in which they live.

Learning outcomes

This chapter explains:

- the importance and key features of person-centred working
- practical ways to provide person-centred support
- how to overcome barriers to person-centred working
- supporting people to make informed choices in their daily life.

The importance of person-centred working

Being person centred in the way that you work means the person you support is at the centre of everything you do. It's about working in a way that the person wants, and helping them to be part of their community. When the person is at the centre, they take the lead, are the most important person, and everyone supporting them is focused on them.

Government policies promote the development of person-centred services and support for all people who receive health and social care support.

Policy reference
Department of
Health White Paper
(2006) *Our Health,
Our Care, Our Say*

Department of
Health White Paper
(2001) *Valuing
People: A New
Strategy for Learning
Disability for the 21st
Century*

The Mental Capacity Act 2005 says that everyone should make their own decisions and should be given all the support they need to help them do so.

The White Paper *Our Health, Our Care, Our Say* (2006) emphasises the need for people who receive care and support to be empowered and enabled to take control of their care. The Paper says, 'Choice means people will increasingly determine what services they want and where.'

In the White Paper *Valuing People* (2001) the government clearly spelled out its priority: 'A person-centred approach… means that planning should start with the individual (not with the service), and take account of their wishes and aspirations.'

Working in a person-centred way should be central to the work of everyone who supports people with learning disabilities. This includes everyone involved, from the care manager and those who develop and plan services, to support workers and local managers.

Direct payments

direct payments
*funding received direct
from local council, so
people can organise
their own support*

Direct payments and individual budgets (self-directed support) are local council payments. These have increased support for people with learning disabilities, who have been assessed as needing social care support. They are for people who want to arrange their own care and support services. These types of support focus totally on the person and their needs.

Individual budget or self-directed support

This is a process that is directly controlled by the individual who receives their own funding following an assessment. Self-directed support means the person makes their own decision about the support and services they need. They have greater choice and control and are at the centre of all decision-making.

Practical ways to provide person-centred support

Being person centred is more than just an approach to working. There are practical ways to provide person-centred support.

Person-centred plans

Person-centred planning is a more structured way for people to plan their lives. It also helps those who provide services and support to understand and work towards people's dreams, aspirations and needs. There are a number of ways for people with

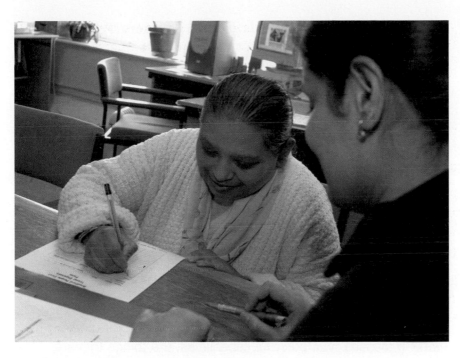

Key point
A person-centred approach means that you should start with the person and take account of their wishes and aspirations in everything you do.

▲ Workers need to support people to take control of their lives.

learning disabilities to develop their own person-centred plan. You may know about the person-centred plans and the planning tools used by the people you support.

Person-centred planning is different from other approaches to planning in a number of ways:

- It focuses on positive aspects of the person.
- The person with a learning disability, or where appropriate a family carer, is in charge of the process.
- Professionals are partners in the process.
- There is an emphasis on finding new and creative ways of solving problems and creating ways of achieving what the person wants.
- The focus is on interdependence.

There are five key features that characterise person-centred planning.

The person is at the centre of the process. This means really listening to the person concerned, learning about the person and understanding their talents, strengths and aspirations. It is about strengthening the person's voice. It involves a commitment to sharing power with the person.

Individual rights, independence and choice are essential. Person-centred working is a rights-based process. Without recognition of the individual's full rights as a citizen and human being, it cannot work.

Family members and friends are full partners. Power sharing involves not only the person, but also family members, friends and other significant people in the person's life. The person at the centre, and those who are important to that person, take the lead role in deciding what opportunities need to be created and what support is required. This involves rethinking the role of the professional. It recognises that the professionals no longer control, but are partners in, the problem-solving process.

Autonomy and interdependence are important. Autonomy means running your own life and making your own decisions. However, none of us is fully autonomous. We all live alongside others who have rights equal to our own. Reliance on one another is an essential aspect of life. Interdependence means people are not seen only as individuals, but individuals within their families and communities.

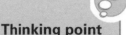

Thinking point
Think how you would feel if other people planned your life and decided what you should do every day. How would you react?

Individual capabilities should be recognised. Person-centred working focuses on a person's capabilities, the things that are important to that person and the support they need. The things people can do are more important than what they cannot do. Person-centred planning leads to continual listening and learning.

Person-centred planning can have a dramatic effect on the lives of people with learning disabilities. It can help them to live their life on their own terms.

Person-centred working

In order to work effectively in a person-centred way, you need to know what person-centred working is and is not about. The table below can help you to see this more clearly.

What is person-centred working?	
What person-centred working is	**What person-centred working is not**
Beginning with and from the person	Professionals take the lead
Creative ways of helping people with learning disabilities realise their aspirations, their hopes and their dreams	Providing the same type of support year in, year out
Making available the support the person needs to achieve the lifestyle they want	Shoehorning individuals into the services that happen to be available, convenient or affordable
Better and more inclusive communities	Focusing on services not people

Overcoming barriers to person-centred working

Being person centred in the way you support people is really important from day one when you work with people with learning disabilities. However, there are a number of factors that can make it difficult to work in a person-centred way. These need to be identified and challenged. Some of these difficulties, and the attitudes people sometimes hold towards people with learning disabilities, are listed below:

Overcoming barriers to person-centred working	
Barriers to person-centred working	**Ways of challenging the barriers**
Protectionism. Keeping people who are a risk to others and themselves away from risk 'for their own good'.	**Encouraging personal growth**. Making choices and having new experiences to develop and grow as a person.
Paternalism. The care of a loving parent, but with all the control and the loss of freedom this implies too.	**Calculated risk-taking**. Deciding which risks are worth taking and which are not is an important part of choice-making and controlling our own lives.
Cocooning. Wrapping people up in cotton wool in case any corners get knocked off.	**Autonomy**. Controlling your own life inevitably involves making a few mistakes, but it's mostly worth it.

There is sometimes a clash between our responsibility as professionals to fulfil our duty of care when supporting people with learning disabilities, and their right to make decisions, even if these involve taking chances or some **risk**. For example, someone might want to learn to use bus services independently, so that they can visit their ageing mother when they wish. There are risks in using public transport for vulnerable people, but why should they not take some chances to be able to visit an elderly parent at times they choose?

risk
how likely it is for a hazard to cause harm

◀ Taking risks can encourage personal growth.

The importance of supporting choice

Your approach to working with a person who has learning disabilities should be based on their rights as a citizen. These include the right to:

- have control over their own life
- make their own choices and decisions
- achieve equality with others
- determine their own future
- learn and grow
- have as much support as is necessary to enable choice.

As part of your work with people with learning disabilities you will often need to reflect on the damaging effects on people of not being able to make choices and decisions about their own lives. You can use the following questions to help you with this:

- What are the negative effects of being overprotected?
- What are the dangers of being underprotected?
- What is the reasonable balance between protection and freedom?

The following are some examples of the negative effects of not enabling people to make decisions about their own lives:

- Challenging behaviour may be a way of communicating wishes and choices that are being ignored by support workers.
- Health problems, such as obesity and other weight problems, may be the result of not knowing enough about healthy food choices.
- Mental health problems can include depressive illness.
- Learned helplessness, or passivity, can lead to a loss of skills and increased demands for support.

Key point

Focusing on the needs and wishes of the person you support will help you overcome any barriers to person-centred working. Challenge situations where others try to fit a person into a service, rather than respecting their needs and dreams. This will also break down barriers to person-centred working.

Scenario: Walks in the country

Philip lives independently in a flat in the centre of a large town. He likes it there because he enjoys the busy environment, and he is well known in the local community. However, during the person-centred planning process Philip says that he enjoys the countryside. He would love to go for walks there, but he never gets the chance to because none of his support workers can drive. They can only go out with him on public transport. After this, a new support worker, Dave, is employed, who has a car. Dave and Philip join a local rambling club and they go for weekly walks in the countryside. Philip has made new friends, and they sometimes pick him up if Dave can't go with him.

How you can support informed choices

There are a number of ways to support people with learning disabilities to make informed choices. One of the most important is helping to remove barriers to communication. If the person you support does not understand what people are saying, or cannot make themselves understood, they cannot make informed choices.

Supporting choice and communication

Communication problems may include difficulties in using or understanding verbal communication and a need for special equipment or skills such as signing. It can also involve personality issues, such as being shy or strongly introverted. The following table is an example of how communication can help someone make informed choices.

Supporting Louise to make informed choices			
Barriers to communication	**Effects on Louise in understanding others**	**Effects on others in understanding Louise**	**Breaking down the barriers to communication**
Louise uses her own version of sign language.	None – she understands other forms of sign language as well.	Many staff, though trained in signing, cannot understand all of her wishes, views, questions, etc.	• Put together a book with photographs of Louise's main personal signs and share this widely with her support workers. • Teach and encourage support workers to learn Louise's own signs and use these together with the more formal signs.
Louise is reluctant to look at people she does not know well.	• She often misses hand-signed information, questions, etc. • She fails to pick up on body language expressed by others.	Louise may sometimes miss responses to her own signings and may only respond to part of the conversation.	• Arrange rotas so that Louise gets to know more staff. • Encourage Louise to make and maintain eye contact in ways that she feels comfortable with.

Activity 4

Identifying communication barriers

Think of a person with learning disabilities you know who has communication difficulties of some kind. Making sure you maintain confidentiality, identify the communication barriers that might prevent the person understanding what is communicated to them, and therefore receiving the necessary information for choice and decision-making.

Think about problems the person might have in communicating to other people what they want or need, therefore preventing them from expressing choice and making decisions.

List actions you could take that might help break down the barriers you identified.

You might find it helpful to summarise your findings in a table like the one on page 37. You may also want to make notes in a notebook.

alternative and augmentative communication

different methods to help people with learning disabilities communicate that are tailored for individuals and used instead of or to supplement speech

Other ways of supporting choice

One way that you can encourage people to make informed choices is by supporting their communication. Other actions you can take are ensuring that:

- the person is at the centre of the way you work
- full account is taken of the person's preferred method of communication
- information is obtained and exchanged in appropriate ways, using **alternative and augmentative communication** where necessary
- you do all you can to ensure the person is in charge of informed decision-making
- the person is properly supported in self-advocacy, or by a citizen advocate
- the focus is on positive aspects of the person's preferences, dislikes, wishes and aspirations
- records are kept of decisions and choices made by the person you support
- the individual is provided with sufficient information to make each choice in a form that they understand.

Key point

Person-centred ways of working should involve all aspects of life that matter to the person.

Helping a person with learning disabilities make informed choices means considering a number of areas of their life:

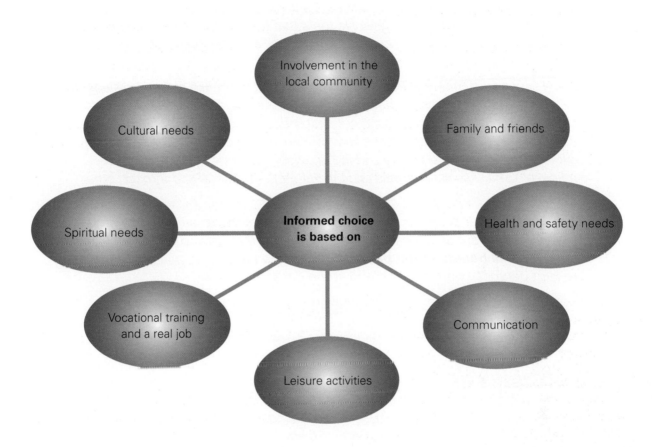

▲ Making informed choices

Supporting choice and decision-making, and working in a person-centred way are important skills for a new learning disability worker to develop. The following is an example of a group of people with learning disabilities living together in the community. Look at their discussion of person-centred working and choice. It should help you to extend the skills you will need to discuss person-centred working, and to support choice in relation to the lives of the people you support.

health action plan
a support plan that sets out a person's health needs and how they should be met

Example 4: Person-centred working and choice

Sam says that person-centred planning has helped him a lot. The main gains he mentions are in lifestyle, work and leisure activities. He now has a job doing things that interest him, which he enjoys. He feels that he can choose what he really wants to do, and this has not always been the case in the past. In his leisure time he does a lot of things he chooses.

Cheryl says that person-centred working has helped her make more of college. In one placement, where she had hoped to study catering, she had ended up washing up all the time. Now she has found out a lot more about what is open to her, and has been able to make her choices known. She had tried a lot of different things. Before, she had often felt angry and fed up. Now she finds that she can discover and develop her special interests and talents, both at college and through other activities.

*As a group, they feel person-centred working is good because it means more activities, going out a lot, doing things and making their own choices. They like the new individual **health action plans** that are being brought in, and the way these are kept personal, both at home and at the doctor's surgery.*

Everyone also seems to think that while many important things, such as health and finances, are very personal, when it comes to some activities, such as trips out and holidays, the individual might often prefer to go with friends in a group.

As in many services, person-centred working is a fairly new development, and both residents and support workers have found it takes a lot of time. But the positive benefits of person-centred working seem clear. Other advantages include avoiding the negative effects of people not being able to make choices about their own lives. It means that support workers may need to provide support for decision-making without influencing the person's choice. This takes skill.

1. Identify from the examples above three positive effects of being able to make choices. What might have been the negative effects if choice and control in their lives had been denied?
2. What methods are described in the examples as ways of enabling people with learning disabilities to make their own choices? For example, providing information and supporting new experiences.
3. From your own experience at work, would you add to these methods? If so, what would you add, and for what reason?

Now turn to the commentary on this example on page 82.

Using support plans

5

'We all know we're moving on from here. We've got to go and that's it. My support plan now is about what I want to do about that, and what comes next for me.'

Steven, *Self-advocate*

Introduction

Many people with learning disabilities now have their own person-centred plans. Their person-centred plan sets out their dreams and aspirations for the future. It tries to find creative ways to bring about change in the person's life, in their community and in the organisations that support them.

One example of providing person-centred support is through a support plan. A support plan is a document that sets out the day-to-day support and care a person needs to achieve the goals and aspirations set out in their person-centred plan. At present, not all support plans are person-centred, but all of them could and should be.

Learning outcomes

This chapter will:

- explain what is meant by a support plan
- describe how you should use a person's support plan in your day-to-day support
- explain the role of the support worker in developing and maintaining a support plan.

What is a support plan?

Planning is a natural part of all our lives. We plan for our free evenings, our careers, our holidays and our retirement. Planning is an organised way of setting out to achieve what we want, and so it is a very useful tool for people with learning disabilities. A support plan is a document that identifies a person's needs and the support required to meet those needs.

A person's support plan should include a number of key areas:

✔ their assessed need
✔ the goals (or objectives) of the support
✔ any risks associated with the person's needs and support
✔ how the support should be provided
✔ a plan for if things go wrong.

Key point
The support plan should set out the main aims and objectives for the person's support. It should also record what has been done and achieved.

Change and support plans

Everyone's life changes, as do their aspirations and expectations. Several of your own childhood and teenage aspirations and dreams will probably have changed. Others will have stayed the same. More abstract things, like 'being happy' or 'being loved', may not have altered. More concrete things, such as 'getting married', 'having children', and 'having my own house', may have changed. For example, 'having my own house' may have now become 'getting a bigger, nicer, or better house' or 'paying off the mortgage'. Or you might be planning to form a new relationship that suits you better than the one that has just ended.

As a result of such changes, the actions we take to realise our aspirations also change. A support plan that suits someone at a particular period of life is going to be less relevant later. The purpose of a support plan is to provide the support the person needs to achieve their goals in life. It will therefore need to be amended as their life progresses.

Life doesn't stop once certain goals, such as a house or a job, have been achieved. Some goals take longer to achieve than others and remain relevant for longer periods. Effective support planning should reflect this. Individual support plans should be regularly reviewed to make sure they are having the desired impact on the person's life. They may need to be adjusted sometimes to find new ways for people to realise their goals.

Support plans should be developed and regularly maintained to ensure that they:

✔ are relevant to the life of the person involved
✔ specify actions and support linked directly to the goals the person wants to achieve at that stage in life
✔ are implemented properly
✔ ensure everyone involved is doing what they should be doing
✔ identify creative ways to solve any problems.

To do this, support plans should be based on carefully collected information. This information is then used both for the initial planning, and for ongoing monitoring and review, which may in turn lead to further planning. Methods of information collection include:

- discussions with the person involved and, if relevant, their advocate
- discussions with family members or carers
- observation of different situations
- telephone and e-mail discussions
- collecting and recording information in paper and computer files

Thinking point
How have your hopes and dreams changed over the years? Why do you think they have changed?

- meetings including as many of the people involved as possible, for example the person receiving the support, relatives, advocates, carers and professionals.

Empathy is a very important skill that a learning disability worker needs when using support plans. It enables the worker to feel what it is like for the person being supported. The following activity will help you with this.

Activity 5

Have your dreams changed?

Think about yourself, past and present, for a few minutes. Write down briefly some words that describe you at ten years old. Who were your heroes? What were your ideas of a perfect day? What were your dreams and aspirations? Now write down some words that describe you today. What are your current dreams? What are your hopes for the future? What is your idea of a perfect day?

Read through your adult dreams and hopes and think about whether these were the same or even relevant when you were younger. Were there things you expected to do that never happened, and opportunities or developments that were unexpected? Or did they change through time as you moved from childhood to adolescence and then into adulthood?

▲ Have your dreams changed?

Support plans and day-to-day support

The things people with learning disabilities want to do for which they already have enough in the way of skills, competence, resources and assistance have probably already been done or put in hand. Support planning can be a way of moving beyond this stage.

One of the main aims of support planning is to enable people with learning disabilities to get the support they need to take more control of their own lives. If this is to happen, we have to make sure that their support plans are based on good information, and keep pace with their life changes. Some changes are brought about by the support plan itself, and the new opportunities it makes available.

Policies and procedures

Your organisation's policies and procedures probably reflect the importance that is given to support plans. You can use these to help you:

- explain why support plans must shape day-to-day support for individuals
- understand your role in developing, implementing and maintaining support plans.

How familiar are you with your own organisation's policies and procedures in relation to individual plans of support? You should know how to obtain copies. Read them and see what your organisation has to say about the following issues.

Relating daily care support to an individual's support plan

It is crucial to remember that support plans can relate to any aspect of a person's life where care or support is required. They should state clearly how much support is needed and how it should be provided. Areas that might be covered include personal care, nutrition, activities, transport, employment and accommodation.

Good support plans will include only the degree of support genuinely needed for the person to achieve a good quality of life. They will avoid providing support that is not needed, or that might prevent individuals from developing skills and abilities. Support can cover almost any activity at any time of day, so plans of support will vary greatly from person to person, and also in relation to each person over time.

Scenario: Andrea's morning support

Andrea has support every morning to help her get up, so she is ready for the day. Her support plan sets out her morning routine in detail. It includes how she likes to be woken up, her washing and dressing routine. It is important to Andrea that the support plan is followed by the three people who work with her. This helps her to learn the routine and join in when she can, for example by holding a flannel or combing her hair.

Recording and reporting unmet needs

As part of your role in helping to develop and maintaining support plans, it is important to identify the needs a person has, but which for one reason or another have not been met. These must then be recorded on the person's file and reported to your supervisor or manager.

The cycle of support planning

If circumstances change substantially a person with learning disabilities, or a carer on their behalf, has the right to ask for a full reassessment to take account of the change in circumstances.

There would be little point in support planning as a single process without follow-up in this way. Some reasons are:

- it would quickly be out of date
- things in life are always changing
- people's needs change with time
- once people have achieved something, they may want to move on
- we need to know if the support plan is working.

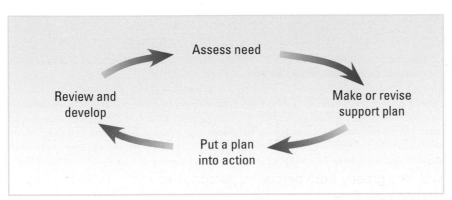

▲ The planning cycle

The planning cycle needs to contain a checking cycle too. This involves monitoring, evaluation and review of the support plan.

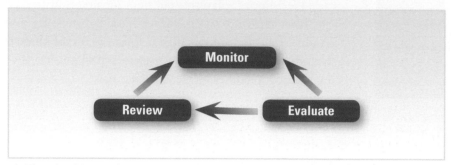

▲ The checking cycle

Monitoring is usually used to describe the regular, even daily, checking of the use and outcomes of a support plan.

Evaluation means comparing those outcomes with the ones that were planned to see that the plan is going ahead as intended.

Reviews take place less frequently than evaluations, usually at specific intervals, and are usually more formal. They involve looking back over the support plan to see:

- if it has been effective in achieving what it was designed for
- which aspects of the plan worked and which did not
- the reasons why certain things worked and others did not
- the areas of the care plan that are still relevant and those that need to be changed.

We can think of a review as a reassessment after an agreed period of time. It is an opportunity to take stock and to decide what change is required in the support plan.

Scenario: Rose's cookery classes

Rose loves cookery and, as part of her support plan, she attends a cookery course for people with learning disabilities at her local college. Sadly, due to changes in funding, the course is closed. Rose is disappointed as she has enjoyed the course and was slowly learning to cook some dishes independently. Her mother finds a course at another college, but this is not specifically designed for people with learning disabilities. Because the course is more challenging, Rose and her support worker are reviewing her support plan.

Your role in support plans

As a learning disability worker you have an important role in developing, maintaining and implementing the support plan of the person you work with. The person's support plan is the main document you should refer to when providing day-to-day support.

As a support worker using a support plan you should:

- become more responsive and supportive, without taking over
- adapt your approach to the person's needs and wishes
- strengthen and support relationships
- constantly re-evaluate your role and contributions
- offer a wider range of options to individuals
- seek innovative and appropriate responses to needs.

> **Key point**
> Good support planning involves assessing need, developing a person-centred plan, putting the plan into action, monitoring, evaluating and reviewing the plan.

Supervision

It is a good idea to discuss support plans during your supervision sessions. These sessions can help you to look at issues related to support plans because it can:

- help you understand the issues better
- encourage you to look at the issues from different standpoints
- enable you to find more ways of involving the person you support.

A support plan is an important tool in providing support for a person with a learning disability. The detailed three-part example below will give you an opportunity to think through the process of developing a support plan, and the role of support workers at each and every stage.

Example 5: Using Elliott's support plan

Paul is a volunteer working with a local advocacy and befriending organisation. Every fortnight he supports Elliott to go out to a concert, to the theatre or to the cinema. Elliott's support plan, that he and his organisation that supports him have shared with Rosie the advocacy co-ordinator, says that Elliott eventually would like to be more independent and go out to events on his own or with a friend from the advocacy group.

Rosie has explained the details of Elliott's support plan to Paul and he supports Elliott to be more independent in buying tickets, finding his place in the theatre and getting the refreshments.

Every three months Elliott, Paul and Rosie have a meeting to review Elliott's support plan and to think about new skills that Elliott wants to develop.

1. What do you think Paul's and Rosie's roles are in using Elliott's support plan?
2. How can Paul and Rosie contribute to Elliott's review of his support plan?

Now turn to the commentary on this example on page 82.

6 The right to take risks

'The first time I caught a bus to town on my own I was so scared. But I'd been shown how, and I did it, and I was so pleased. Now I go when I want to buy my CDs and have a coffee. You just have to know what you're doing, that's all.'

Annie, *Self-advocate*

Introduction

Risk is like stress. It's necessary in the right amounts, but potentially damaging if overdone. Sometimes when you are supporting a person with a learning disability, there can seem to be a conflict between your professional duty of care towards them, and their right to take the risks they choose. Because of this, the care of people with learning disabilities has traditionally avoided risk. Nowadays, we recognise that considered and managed risk can add enormously to someone's quality of life.

Learning outcomes

This chapter explores:

- the principle that people have the right to take risks
- the negative effects on people of not having the opportunity to take risks
- why people with learning disabilities have often not been allowed or encouraged to take risks
- the benefits of risk-taking.

The principle of the right to take risks

Our understanding of learning disabilities has changed substantially over recent years. Our approach to risk-taking of all kinds has changed along with it. By encouraging and supporting well-informed risk-taking we are providing the opportunity for people to experience success, deal with failure and learn from both positive and negative experiences. People will become more resilient as a result of learning from their experiences.

Historical attitudes to risk-taking

Historically, many people were cared for in large institutions, such as hospitals or segregated village communities. Everything was provided on the premises, so there was little need for any contact with the outside world.

Typical beliefs were:

- people with learning disabilities required protection from the risks they might encounter in the outside world, such as exploitation and abuse
- they themselves presented a risk to other people
- they posed a risk to themselves, either because of their disability or because of their behaviour
- these risks would be best managed within an institution and by specially trained medical staff.

As a consequence, people's exposure to the risks of ordinary life experiences was carefully controlled. Unfortunately, we now know from enquiries into abuse and ill-treatment that many people with learning disabilities faced greater risks inside the institutions than they might have outside them.

The negative effects of protecting people from all risk

In some situations, such as handling money and bills, there is still a tendency towards overprotection today, which many people with learning disabilities find stifling. This tendency also applies to the expression of sexuality. However, current attitudes to risk of all kinds are changing.

Not allowing people to take risks is an easy but misguided option. It is not one that most people would choose. Not enabling people to take risks, or protecting them from reasonable risk-taking, denies them their rights as equal and valued adults. The message we are giving, to them and to others, is that they are incapable and dependent.

When we do not enable people with learning disabilities to take risks, or do not provide them with choice about risk-taking, we:

- deny them their rights
- deprive them of valuable and enjoyable learning experiences
- reduce their ability to deal with the unforeseen risks they will inevitably encounter in life
- put them in a position of inequality, dependency, disempowerment and inferiority.

Such an approach also denies people the right to control their own life, make their own decisions and learn from their experiences.

Key point

Risk means the likelihood of an event or circumstances causing harm to the person involved or other people, including all forms of abuse, neglect and exploitation.

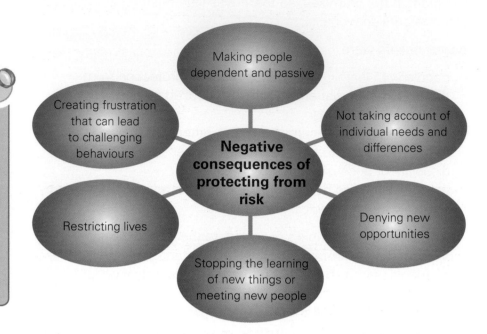

Making people dependent and passive

Creating frustration that can lead to challenging behaviours

Not taking account of individual needs and differences

Negative consequences of protecting from risk

Restricting lives

Denying new opportunities

Stopping the learning of new things or meeting new people

▲ Some negative consequences of never having the opportunity to take risks

Why people have been discouraged from risk-taking

People who have a learning disability have often not been allowed or encouraged to take risks. There are many reasons for this.

Dependency

Often it was felt that, because of their disability and consequent need for support, some people faced additional risks. However, many people with learning disabilities are at more risk precisely because of their limited experience. They have little understanding of potential dangers, partly because of their dependency on others for many aspects of their lives.

Negativity and social barriers

Risks often arise, not because of the person's learning disability, but because of negative images of and attitudes towards people with disabilities. This means that people with learning disabilities face the risk of exploitation, discrimination and abuse by others.

Some attitudes and resulting barriers to positive risk-taking
People who require help with intimate personal care are more vulnerable to physical and sexual abuse.
People who have difficulty communicating verbally are in a more vulnerable position because they are less able to tell someone about abuse.
People who have difficulty understanding money are at risk of making simple, but costly, mistakes or of financial abuse.
People using services of all sorts are at risk of being treated unfairly, exploited, abused, denied their rights and controlled by others.
Some people with learning disabilities are extremely trusting of people who appear to have authority over them, and so are at greater risk of exploitation or abuse.
Some people with learning difficulties find it difficult to understand the consequences of their own actions, or those of other people.
Many people with learning disabilities continue to live at home with family carers, some of whom may be anxious about their son or daughter taking risks.

Thinking point
Think about risks you take in your own life. Are you a cautious person? Do you think carefully about the consequences of your actions, or do you like to go in at the deep end?

Protection from risk within society

As citizens, we expect protection from some risks within our own society. For example, we expect protection from the police, our legal system, regulatory bodies and state-run organisations. We are protected against buying faulty goods, or from bogus doctors, and expect the police to act when we are burgled or assaulted. People with learning disabilities are entitled to the same protection from risks in law and in society as the rest of us. Equally, like the rest of society, they should not be prevented from taking properly assessed and managed risks. To do so would deny them many potential benefits.

Risk and the duty of care

Everyone who provides social or health care has a duty of care to the people they support or their patients. Duty of care means that workers must take reasonable care to avoid acts or omissions that are likely to cause harm to the person they care for or to another person.

As a support worker working with people who have learning disabilities you have a duty of care, just as your colleagues do. This does not mean that you should prevent people taking risks. It does mean that these risks should be assessed and managed as part of planning and everyday work. It also means that you can be held responsible if it is found that you have failed in your duty of care to someone you support.

Duty of care may conflict with the right of the individual to take risks. There may be times when you decide that your duty of care needs to take precedence over the rights of the individual. If so, you have a responsibility to discuss this with the individual concerned and with your manager. This will provide you with guidelines for further action within the policies and procedures of your organisation.

Scenario: Is going out too risky?

Nigel lived at home with his elderly parents until he was 42. His parents lived a quiet life, rarely going out at night and seeing few friends and relations. When Nigel moved into his own flat he wanted to do things, such as go out to the cinema and for meals with friends, that he hadn't been able to do before. Nigel's parents thought that this was too risky. John, Nigel's support worker, helped Nigel and his parents think through the opportunities and risks in more detail.

Policies and procedures

risk assessment
identifying and recording possible risks and deciding how to manage them

Many of the points we have looked at in relation to risk are both difficult to get right in practice, and very important. Often, there are legal implications and standards that must be met by law. For this reason, policies and procedures dealing with **risk assessment** and management need to be clear, accurate, readily available to staff and used in practical day-to-day work.

When looking at the policies and procedures of your organisation you should ask yourself whether they:

- mention legal requirements in relation to risk management
- define the values that underlie the organisation's approach to risk
- state the responsibilities of the organisation to safeguard people and minimise risk
- provide clear guidance to managers and workers at all levels on their duties and responsibilities in relation to risk-taking
- explain how the people with learning disabilities your service works with and their families and friends can know about these, and how they will be involved in decisions relating to risk.

If you cannot satisfy yourself on all these points, or if anything is unclear to you, you should raise this with your line manager or a senior member of staff.

Activity 6

Read your organisation's policies and procedures

Get hold of a copy of your organisation's policy and procedures on risk. How easy was it to do that? How easy would it be for other staff or volunteers, particularly those who are new, inexperienced or untrained? Do the family and friends of the people you support know about these polices and procedures? Does the person you support know about these policies? Is there an easy-read version?

Key point

Risk-taking can have benefits. This makes it an important and potentially productive aspect of supporting people with a learning disability.

The benefits of risk-taking

You may think that taking risks has only negative results and should always be avoided. However, taking risks can bring benefits.

Current attitudes towards risk-taking and people with learning disabilities

Some negative attitudes undoubtedly persist, but most of us recognise the need for a balance between people having the freedom to encounter and manage different kinds and levels of risk, and sensible protection from risk.

Our attitudes towards risk-taking in relation to people with learning disabilities have changed as a result of several factors. In particular, there have been changes in our understanding of learning disabilities and the way services are provided. There is also a greater recognition of the rights of people with learning disabilities. We realise that people with learning disabilities have the right to control their own lives. This means they will encounter risk in the same way as everybody else, and will learn from both positive and negative consequences of risk-taking.

If people with learning disabilities are to experience and manage risk, it is important to discuss situations with the person's family and friends. Everyone needs to understand their perceptions of risk and ways of identifying and managing risk. This will lead to fewer misunderstandings and a shared view of the risk and the potential consequences. Many family carers can give information of earlier strategies used to manage risk. Involving these people shows respect for them as equal partners.

How people benefit from taking risks

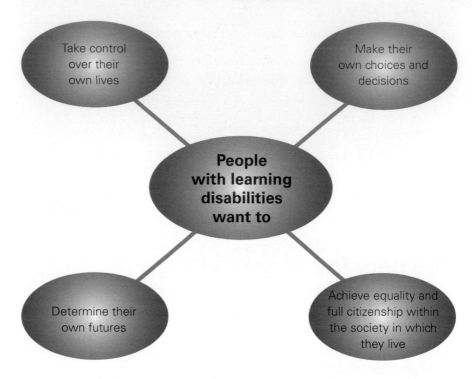

Although you cannot actually empower people, you can enable them to empower themselves. Giving people the opportunity to take assessed risks so they achieve their treasured goals and dreams is one way of doing this.

Risk-taking is an essential element in this process of empowerment and self-determination. Risk-taking can bring the following benefits to people with learning disabilities:

- learning to identify and deal with different levels of risk
- learning from the consequences of risk, both positive and negative
- the satisfaction and achievement of success
- new experiences
- making new relationships
- the creation of new opportunities through trying out new things
- becoming better equipped to deal with life
- growth and development as a person.

Additional potential benefits can come, as the person's skills increase, through managed risk-taking. These include developing independence, finding new opportunities for learning, better choice- and decision-making, a sense of achievement, learning more advanced skills, managing their own lives and increasing variety in their lives.

▲ Managed risk-taking allows the development of new skills.

Key point
When people with a learning disability are not provided with choice and information about risk-taking, or are protected from taking risks, we deny them their rights.

Scenario: Keith develops his drama skills

Keith loves drama. For some time he has belonged to a drama group at college that only involves people with a learning disability. Keith has recently joined a local amateur dramatic group run by his lecturer. This has given him more opportunities to develop his skills and meet more people who share his passion. Keith's mother and his support worker, Pam, are all keen to support him to develop his skills and they are working with him to identify and manage any possible risks.

Avoiding unnecessary risk

Recognising the right of people with learning disabilities to take risks doesn't remove our responsibilities as support workers to minimise high-risk factors, or to ensure safeguards are in place. But it does mean that we always treat people with learning disabilities as adults, with freedom of choice and equal rights within society.

Inevitably, this means that people will encounter varying kinds and degrees of risk, some of which will have adverse consequences. We have already looked at possible exploitation. Other potential **hazards** include loneliness, discrimination and failure. In our work with people with learning disabilities we must be clear about why

hazard
anything that could cause harm to a person

we are allowing, encouraging or supporting risk. We must be certain that people are not exposed to unnecessary risk because of our negligence or oversight.

Most services are striving to provide people with learning disabilities with the best possible opportunities for empowerment and independence, and to support them in achieving their aspirations. Risk-taking is a creative and productive part of this process.

The higher the expectations and opportunities within the support people receive, the greater the risk. The opposite is also true. In a culture of overprotection, low expectations and low levels of participation from people who use the service, it is less likely that people will be allowed to take risks.

The example that follows gives you an opportunity to reflect on some of the challenges people with learning disabilities, families, support workers and organisations face when considering the topic of risk.

Example 6: Recognising the right to take risks

The Beech Tree Centre caters for 20 people with learning disabilities. Every so often an outing is planned. A bus is hired and all the people who use the service and all the support workers go together. Once at their destination, they split into three groups, each with two workers and sometimes a volunteer helper. Everyone has the same amount of money to spend. Workers look after the money and pay for what people want to buy. The whole group meets for lunch at a pre-arranged place and all have the same meal, which has been booked in advance.

Families of the people with learning disabilities are happy with the service as they know their relatives are safe and well looked after for long periods of time. They appreciate the overall package that is offered, but some feel that their relative is not treated as the individual that they are. Most of the people with learning disabilities are also happy and defer to the workers most of the time. There is generally a happy and relaxed atmosphere in the centre. Everyone has an individual programme, most of which takes place in the centre, although there are regular visits to the library, a local leisure centre and other venues in the neighbourhood for small groups of people.

The Four Acres Centre provides less traditional day opportunities for people with learning disabilities. It used to operate in the same way as the Beech Tree Centre, but now has a very different approach and programmes. Outings with people are rarely planned. Instead, their building acts as a resource centre and a base where people spend only some of their time, when it suits them. Some people never go

continued ▶

there. Instead, workers go to them to see how they are getting on in their job or voluntary work, or to review their programmes with them.

Because of this flexibility, many more people now use the centre, but not all of them take all of the services it has to offer. Individual support plans are based on person-centred approaches, combined with risk assessment and management. They include part-time and voluntary work, all sorts of community activities and some centre-based activity. In the evening, the centre acts as a drop-in venue where people plan and carry out their own activities. When this method of working was first adopted, some people with learning disabilities and many parents complained that it took away services and it was more risky. However, all the people who use the service and most families seem now to have adjusted to the new system. Some families' accounts of how risks have been managed in other settings developed the workers' ideas of what was possible.

1. What are the negative consequences of not allowing people to take risks?
2. Why do you think, despite this, that both the people with learning disabilities and most of their families seem happy with what the Beech Tree Centre provides? List three reasons.
3. What are the potential benefits to people with learning disabilities of the Four Acres Centre?
4. What are the potential hazards to people with learning disabilities of a service like the Four Acres Centre?
5. Why do you think the change to a more person-centred service might cause problems?
6. Write down your ideas and discuss them with your line manager or an experienced colleague.

Now turn to the commentary on this example on page 83.

7

Risk assessment

Introduction

Every day we assess risks, and make decisions as a result, even though we may not be aware of doing so. When supporting people with learning disabilities, it is important that you think about whether a particular course of action or activity will present a risk to them or others. Your organisation will have formal risk assessment procedures to help the person being supported, their family and friends and the people supporting them to both understand and plan for risks.

You should be familiar with the risk procedures of your organisation, and with the need to keep up to date with them.

Learning outcomes

This chapter explains:

- how and when to use risk assessment procedures when providing support
- who to involve in a risk assessment process
- the need to inform others about risk
- reviewing and updating risk assessments.

How and when to use risk assessment procedures

Procedures are the written methods by which the organisation's policies are carried out on a day-to-day basis. They are there to ensure that everything necessary is done in the right order, at the right time and in a way which is recognised as good practice. They make providing good support to people easier.

Understanding and using your organisation's risk assessment policy and procedures to assess whether the behaviour or activities of a person presents a risk to themselves or others is an important part of a support worker's role.

The main principles of risk assessment are:

- Risk assessment should be an integral part of planning.
- The person with a learning disability should be fully involved.
- The assessment should define the type and level of risk.
- The assessment should identify both the positive and negative consequences of an action and ways to minimise risk.
- Risk assessments should be recorded and regularly reviewed.

Policies and procedures concerning risk-taking

Risk assessment is a vital part of planning, and should involve the person with learning disabilities. As we have seen in Chapter 6, every organisation should have policies and procedures that relate to risk-taking. These should include the values underpinning the service's approach to risk-taking. There should also be clear procedures and guidelines for assessing and managing risk. Some of these requirements are governed by law. For example, managers and employers have legal responsibilities under the Health and Safety Act.

Risk management

Your employer's policy on managing risk should include a statement outlining their principles, beliefs and approach in relation to risk management. It should provide people with learning disabilities, support workers and family carers with the information they need to make judgements and decisions about risk-taking.

By nature, policies consist of general statements. In order for policies to be converted into action, the employer must also have ways of putting them into effect. These ways are often referred to as procedures. There should also be a set of guidelines that will help you to follow these procedures in your own work.

Policies and procedures dealing with risk assessment and management should:

- meet legal requirements
- define the values that underlie the organisation's approach to risk management, such as empowerment, autonomy, rights, self-determination, safeguarding people and minimising risk
- describe the organisation's goals, aims and objectives in enabling and supporting risk-taking and how these are shared with the people who are being supported, their families and friends
- describe the processes by which those goals, aims and objectives will be achieved
- identify procedures for dealing with the consequences of risk-taking

Thinking point
When you are planning to go somewhere you haven't been before (for example, for a night out with friends) do you think about the possible risks? Do you plan how you are going to get home safely?

Policy reference
Health and Safety at Work Act 1974

- provide clear guidance to workers at all levels on their duties and responsibilities in relation to risk-taking.

You are not likely to be responsible for formulating policy or identifying procedures for implementing the risk management policy. This is the job of the managers in your service or organisation. However, you may be asked to contribute your views, based on your experiences in work. You will definitely have a responsibility for following risk management procedures and upholding your employer's policy in all aspects of your work.

Knowing about risk management policy and procedures

You should be familiar with your organisation's policies and procedures. You should know where to find them and be able to describe how to use them. This means you should:

- consider risk-taking as an integral part of your work
- be fully informed about the service's strategies for dealing with risk-taking
- assess your day-to-day work and practice against the service's risk-taking policies and procedures
- apply these policies and procedures in all aspects of your work
- know who to go to for assistance in the event of uncertainty or an emergency.

You should be able to outline your service's risk management policy and procedures and describe how you would use the approved risk assessment procedures in a variety of situations.

Using risk assessment procedures with people

Risk assessment and management involves:

- ✔ identifying the potential benefits for the person concerned of an activity, event or situation
- ✔ identifying the potential hazards or things that could go wrong
- ✔ weighing up the likelihood of things going wrong
- ✔ taking steps to reduce the risk
- ✔ helping the person make decisions based on these factors
- ✔ in special circumstances, making decisions for people
- ✔ having contingency plans for dealing with problems should they arise.

If all these requirements seem a little confusing, remember that the basic principles are similar to those for any form of management.

Thinking point

We assess and manage risk all the time in our own lives, but we probably don't think of it as risk management. How do you assess risk in your own life, and what steps do you take to manage the risks you identify?

The process of assessing and managing risk can be broken down into stages:

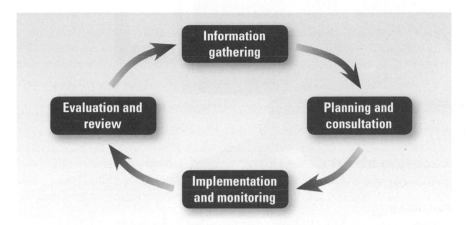

▲ The risk management process

Some of these activities will overlap. For example, consultation with the family may provide extra information. Or evaluation may provide ideas for new plans. This is inevitable, and a good thing. Properly carried out, risk management is a cyclical process like person-centred planning, and of course should form part of person-centred working practices.

A checklist is a useful way of ensuring nothing is forgotten in carrying out a process like risk assessment and management. But this assumes that we know that risk is present in a situation and needs to be prepared for. The nature of life is that sometimes we are not prepared for something that occurs. We need to be aware that this can happen. We need to know what to do when we encounter unplanned risk in our work.

Activity 7

Examining risky situations

Think of someone you have worked with and a risky situation where you were involved. This need not be something dramatic like abseiling or hang-gliding. Everyday life has its risks, too, great and small. For example, a young man you work with may want to go clubbing with friends, or a young woman may want to learn to use the bus service to help her find a job.

Examine the process you, your colleagues and the person with a learning disability went through.

▲ Everyday life has its risks, too, great and small.

Unplanned risk assessment

Although risk assessment should ideally happen as part of planning, real life doesn't always work like this. Sometimes risk assessment happens in response to an emergency, as part of crisis management.

Scenario: Storm damage

During a severe storm, one of the trees in the road outside a residential care home fell and damaged the garage. Fortunately, no one was injured, but some of the residents heard the tree fall and were upset by what happened. Because the structure of the building could have been affected, the residents had to stay in other houses owned by the same organisation for several days. They could not return until the building had been thoroughly checked, the tree removed and the garage repaired. After this event the staff and the people who lived in the house evaluated what went well during the evacuation, what could have been done better and what they should do next time. This enabled them to put in place a new plan for a temporary evacuation of the building.

Sometimes unexpected things happen that have negative consequences. Correct responses can minimise these, and may even result in positive outcomes from the situation.

Risk assessment is very important when unplanned risks arise. Your role and the reasons to do risk assessments at times like these are to:

- identify the risks in the current situation
- help find ways of dealing with any adverse consequences that have occurred
- provide support to reduce the risks and negative consequences associated with them in the future
- record and report decisions and the reasons for them
- set up monitoring procedures so that any additional or recurring adverse consequences are dealt with immediately.

Each service will have its own requirements, as well as those relating to laws of health and safety. As a general rule, when informing others about risks identified and actions taken when unplanned risks occur you should:

- ✔ follow the guidelines of your own service
- ✔ describe precisely what happened and your response
- ✔ explain your decision
- ✔ describe what happened as a result of your decision
- ✔ say how you explained your decision to the person you were supporting
- ✔ state who else was involved in the incident
- ✔ state who you reported to or otherwise informed
- ✔ date and sign the report
- ✔ make sure the report goes to the right people
- ✔ list on all copies of the report everyone who has had a copy.

Key point
Unplanned decisions about risk and any actual or potential outcomes should be reported to your line manager and all other people affected by the decision. The person you support should know about any decisions if they were not involved in the decision-making.

Who to involve in risk assessment

You may have had experience of risk assessment in your own work. This may have been informally in your everyday interaction with people with learning disabilities, or it may have been in more formal risk assessment situations, possibly as part of planning. Your exact involvement will depend on various things, including how well risk is managed in your own service and the kind of work you do. Risk assessment is more prevalent in some types of work settings than in others. For example, if you work with people whose behaviour challenges, risk assessment will be a regular part of your work. You may have to assess the risk to the person, to those working with them and to others, plus the risks of undertaking certain activities or using certain approaches.

Involving people with learning disabilities in risk assessment

It is important to find ways of including the person with learning disabilities as fully as possible in the risk assessment process. They should always be involved with anything that concerns their lives. It is up to those who work with them to find ways of doing this which suit individual needs and abilities.

All records relevant to risk assessment and management should be accessible to the person with learning disabilities. This might mean finding other ways of presenting them so that the person can understand. For example, they might need to be on audio-tape, in simpler language, or large print or using signing or symbols.

Others who might be involved

As with other forms of planning, it is an important principle to ask the person whose plan it is who they wish to have involved. Other people who might be involved include family members or other support workers, citizen advocates or self-advocacy supporters. Community nursing or behavioural support teams, social workers, key workers in health and social support, employers, tutors or trainers, the GP, police, neighbours and any other agencies concerned might also be involved. In some situations in the community postal workers, shopkeepers, pub and café staff, refuse collectors, milk delivery workers, bus drivers and so on, can provide useful support.

Informing others about risk identification and assessment

You should keep clear and accurate records and make sure that these are available to everyone involved who needs to see them. This, of course, is subject to the usual rules on confidentiality, and the consent of the person who is the subject of the records.

Who you should report to

Who you need to report to depends on the circumstances, and on who is affected by your risk identification. You will always have to report to your manager, or to the senior colleague who has assumed responsibility if your manager is away. Assessments about risk-taking and its actual or possible outcomes should be reported to:

- the person concerned
- your line manager
- any other senior colleague responsible for procedures
- all other people affected by the decision, which could include family carers and friends.

You may also have to report to some or all of the following people:

- other colleagues, including those at other organisations that support the person
- relatives or other carers of the person involved
- advocacy workers
- those responsible for the venue or situation if an incident could occur or has occurred there
- social services or the social work department
- community support teams
- the police – where you think there has been a criminal offence.

Systems for keeping people informed

Recording and reporting in risk assessment and management is important. Keeping records is fundamental to informing people about risk. Some or all of the following could be relevant. Other records might be added, depending on circumstances:

▲ Good risk management opens opportunities.

As a support worker working with people who have learning disabilities, you have a responsibility to:

- keep records of all of your decisions involving risk-taking
- ensure that all records are up to date and contain all the necessary information
- complete all the risk management records required by your organisation's policies and procedures on risk
- pass on to appropriate and authorised people any information on risks identified.

Using guidelines on recording and reporting

The procedures in your workplace should tell you what records you are expected to complete, and who to inform about any risks identified. If you are unsure of the position at any time, you must discuss this as soon as possible with your line manager or supervisor.

You have seen how to record risk assessments, and who to inform. These are the main reasons why this should be done:

- Everyone involved should be aware of the assessment, know who made it, and why.
- The person with learning disabilities has the right to understand and object to your assessment.
- Your line manager and other senior colleagues need this information to oversee your work.
- Your manager has a duty to ensure that you have not infringed the person's rights, and that your decision is justified.
- There might be differing opinions about your assessment that need to be resolved.
- Your decision might affect other aspects of the person's life, or other people.
- Other people might have to take action as a result of your assessment.

Informing about unplanned decisions on risk-taking

However well you assess risks and plan for them, there will almost certainly be times when you have to make unplanned decisions and interventions in relation to risk-taking. It is important to record and fully inform others who need to know about unplanned risks and the way you handled them.

Confidentiality

One additional point to be aware of here is the potential conflict with confidentiality when reporting assessments and decisions about risk. There are occasions when breaching confidentiality will be unavoidable. On other occasions you may have to act

Key point
Unplanned decisions about risk should be recorded to ensure that everyone concerned is aware of the action, who made it and why. Recording risk assessments means appropriate follow-up action can be taken. It provides information for future risk assessment and it safeguards you.

immediately, with no time to think about confidentiality. When this happens, make sure that you discuss the situation as soon as possible with your line manager, so that any breach of confidentiality can be dealt with. (See Chapter 8 for more information about confidentiality.)

Reviewing and updating risk assessments

Life is full of change – we grow older, we learn new skills, have more interests, we meet new friends. As we change, we encounter fresh challenges and risks, and some old risks fall by the wayside. Risk for all of us is a constantly shifting thing, and the more people with learning disabilities participate in everyday life, the more this applies to them also. It is a reflection of our success in helping someone to lead a fuller life that frequent review and updating of risk assessment for that person is necessary.

Reviews are different from regular monitoring in that they take place less frequently, and are more formal. They are also more likely to lead to changes in the risk assessment and risk management arrangements. Sometimes, however, monitoring identifies that major changes are leading to a situation where an early review is required.

Common factors in a well-planned risk assessment review are:

- It will be scheduled well in advance so that all concerned can plan to be present.
- Because of its importance, extra efforts will be made to ensure the presence of the person concerned, family, advocate and key worker.
- It will have an agenda and background papers in a format the person concerned can understand. These will be circulated in advance to all attending.
- The last risk assessment will act as a baseline for the review, which will focus on any relevant changes since that assessment.
- It will be conducted at a speed the person concerned can cope with to ensure they understand and agree with what is being discussed.
- The outcome will be geared to a fresh risk assessment, which will be confidential, but circulated to all who need to see it.

Failure to update a risk assessment may place the individual concerned in a worse position than if none had been carried out. This is because support staff, the family and other carers could be working with a false sense of security. They may think that the main risks have been identified and evaluated, and that there are adequate systems in place to deal with them. It is sometimes better to know that there are gaps and to be alert for them, rather than to be under the mistaken impression that all precautions necessary have been taken.

The new risks may be worse than the old ones, and require greater precautions. Or, on the other hand, risks may have declined and fewer protective measures may therefore be needed. Poor practice in reviewing and updating may obviously place someone at greater risk, but it can also deny people opportunities that might be opened to them by good up-to-date risk assessment.

So many different aspects of an individual's life can affect the review and updating of a risk assessment that it is worth establishing some key areas that should regularly be looked at.

Personality

Some people are more likely to behave in ways which could be described as risky because of their personality. For example, they may be more likely to take part in extreme sports, or to lose control of their emotions easily. Personality can change with factors such as time, use of medication and life events.

Physical health

As we get older, the risks associated with ill health increase. With medical advances, more people with learning disabilities are living longer, but they may encounter health risks in later life which require review.

Mental health

In some people, changes in their mental health may affect the risks they present to themselves or to others. This may be for the better or for the worse. The early onset of dementia in some people with learning disabilities is an increasing and continually changing risk factor.

Emotional well-being

Many people with learning disabilities have to deal with major losses and bereavements in life, including frequent moves of home and changes in support workers. These are often not recognised, and so not properly resolved. They can affect physical and mental health, family life, behaviour and relationships of all kinds for many years afterwards. Similar problems can arise as a result of isolation and boredom, which are still all too common, even today.

Family life

As with all of us, a supportive family is greatly beneficial to someone with a learning disability. However, change affects family life all the time and may well result in situations where risk changes, too. Families also change when people move on, when parents divorce, or when a parent or a sibling dies.

Relationships

Friendships or other relationships formed by individuals may be positive and important but increase the chance of risk being encountered. This may be particularly so with a strong bond between two people. It is important to be aware of this, and to support the person in managing the risks we all face in relationships.

Communication skills

Communication skills may improve or decline over time. They have a direct impact on the review of risk assessments because of the huge importance of communication.

Understanding risk, and the ways to assess and manage risk, are part of everyday life, and part of your responsibilities as a learning disability worker. The example below will help you think about how you manage risk in your day-to-day work.

Example 7: Using risk assessment procedures

Leah is going to do voluntary work for the first time and will be travelling alone. As preparation, her support worker Janelle is supporting her to practise her bus journey. In line with her support plan, Leah is learning where to catch the bus near her home, which bus to catch, what fare to pay, where the bus stops near her work and the short route to work from where she gets off.

Leah and Janelle plan this together and travel together initially. Once Leah is confident, Janelle arranges to meet her at the bus stop. Then Janelle will wait at work or at Leah's home. The plan is that Leah will eventually travel by herself to and from her voluntary work, using her own money for the fare.

Leah takes time to learn new skills. She also takes time to learn how to transfer skills into new situations. Because of this she and her family and the support workers working on her support plan have decided not to try to teach her more than these stages until she has settled into the routine of travelling to and from

continued ▶

work. It has been left to Janelle to decide when the plan should be reviewed and, if necessary, updated.

1. Bearing in mind all you have learned about risk assessment and planning, note down three possible risks that Leah and Janelle might identify.

2. Briefly describe how Janelle, Leah and her family might assess and manage the three potential risks you have identified.

Now turn to the commentary on this example on page 84.

Principles and practice of confidentiality

8

'What staff write about me is personal and private. Not to be passed on. I can see it, but not other people. I feel really strongly about this.'

Annie, *Self-advocate*

Introduction

Confidentiality is one of the most sensitive issues relating to working with and supporting people with learning disabilities. In the past, people with learning disabilities had little or no privacy in their lives. Now they are increasingly aware of their right to privacy. Any breach of it could seriously damage your relationship with the person you support.

Support workers should keep comprehensive and accurate records and make sure that these are available to everyone involved who needs to see them. However, it is important to follow the rules on confidentiality, and to obtain the consent of the person who is the subject of the records.

Learning outcomes

This chapter explains:

- why confidentiality is important
- the principles of confidentiality and when these might need to be breached
- understanding policies and procedures about sharing information
- practical ways to support a culture of confidentiality.

Why confidentiality is important

Stop for a minute and think just how much you know about the personal lives of the people with learning disabilities you work with. Imagine how you would feel if someone had similar confidential information about you. It could include all your personal history (possibly even details of your birth), your family background, assessments showing what you can and cannot do, personal medical information, and many other aspects of your life. You would feel exposed and very much at the mercy of that person, wouldn't you?

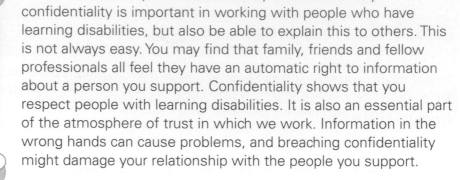

Thinking point
Can you keep things confidential? Do you sometimes confuse sharing information with gossip?

Thinking point
Think of a situation where it would be important for someone to disclose information about you that should otherwise be kept confidential.

It is essential that you should not only understand why confidentiality is important in working with people who have learning disabilities, but also be able to explain this to others. This is not always easy. You may find that family, friends and fellow professionals all feel they have an automatic right to information about a person you support. Confidentiality shows that you respect people with learning disabilities. It is also an essential part of the atmosphere of trust in which we work. Information in the wrong hands can cause problems, and breaching confidentiality might damage your relationship with the people you support.

What is meant by confidentiality

As a support worker you are in a trusted position, and have access to very personal information about individuals and their families, all of which is confidential. Confidentiality means respecting personal information about individuals, their families and carers. It means keeping this information private, and not disclosing it unless an appropriate person, or people, gives you permission to do so. This will usually be the person with a learning disability, unless the person cannot consent.

Confidentiality must be maintained at all times when you are working. It is part of doing a professional job, and something which you agreed to when you were appointed. You may get into trouble if you disclose information to the wrong people.

When confidentiality may need to be breached

You should never normally breach confidentiality. However, there are times when you may have to do this. For example, if you suspect someone is being abused you must report it, even if you think the person who told you about it will not be happy. Always seek guidance from managers or from senior colleagues if managers are not available.

Limits and boundaries to confidentiality

Key point
Confidentiality is important because everyone has a right to privacy and dignity.

As confidentiality and trust are so important when working with people with learning disabilities, it may be wise to establish limits to confidentiality from the outset. This would need to involve not only the person with a learning disability, but family, other close carers and line managers. Advocacy workers often deal with this by making it clear from their first involvement that they will maintain confidentiality, except in certain clear circumstances. This is a useful example to follow.

Scenario: Following procedures

Delroy works with Clive regularly on a one-to-one basis. Clive tells Delroy that he is afraid of his uncle, but will not tell him why. In this case Delroy must follow his organisation's procedures about the protection of vulnerable adults. It is possible that Clive is not being abused but, as there is a chance that abuse may be happening, Delroy must breach confidentiality.

One dilemma is that where people have severe or profound learning disabilities, they may be particularly vulnerable to situations where confidentiality has to be breached. But they themselves may not understand, or may find it difficult to communicate about, issues of confidentiality. However, this is no reason not to maintain the principles and practices of confidentiality so far as possible.

With the best will in the world, times are bound to occur when confidentiality needs to be breached. So much depends on circumstances and what would happen if you did, or did not, pass on information. Activity 8 illustrates this.

Activity 8

Questions of confidentiality

Read the brief descriptions below of situations that can occur in day-to-day working. Discuss each of them with a work colleague, and try to decide whether confidentiality should be breached in these situations or not.

For each question, write brief notes. Your answer may not be a clear or final one. This is often the case in these circumstances in real life. For example, if you feel more information should be obtained, or that others need to be consulted, say how you would go about arranging this. Would your approach involve some breach of confidentiality in itself? How would you justify this?

You act as key worker for Marie. Your line manager has suggested that you pass on to a worker in another organisation some information about her which you feel should be kept private. Should you do as instructed?

Neelam attends your day centre. She has complex physical and learning disabilities and is highly dependent on carers for personal care needs. Should you pass on information about her personal habits and the way she communicates her needs to staff at the leisure centre she attends once a week?

Rory has just finished school and is moving on to college. His siblings have a history of petty crime and you are concerned that he might be drawn into this lifestyle as he gets older. Should you pass this information on to college staff?

One point you should pick up from this activity is that making a decision on confidentiality is hard. Thinking carefully about it will help you not only decide, but be ready to defend that decision.

Breaching confidentiality

Below are some principles on which you can base your thinking and decisions about breaching confidentiality:

- the degree of risk that someone will come to significant harm
- the balance between the person's right to confidentiality, and the danger that will result if you do not disclose information
- the balance between risk-taking and the duty of care
- whether or not the person is competent to decide, and has given informed consent
- the views of family, friends and any advocate
- the views of your senior managers and experienced colleagues.

Note that you should not come to a decision alone. Except in rare cases where an emergency decision has to be reached, it is standard good practice to consult with the person involved and others concerned.

Understanding your organisation's confidentiality policies and procedures

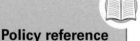

Policy reference
The Data Protection Act 1998

Every organisation takes confidentiality very seriously and should have policies and procedures that tell staff what is required of them. This information should also be available to the people who use your service, as well as family carers and friends. The Data Protection Act 1998 has guidelines your organisation needs to follow when collecting and storing confidential information.

If policies and procedures are to work well, people have to know them and use them. The following is a checklist to test your knowledge of your organisation's policies and procedures on confidentiality. See if you can answer the questions confidently, without referring to the documentation.

- ✔ Where are your organisation's policies and procedures on confidentiality normally kept, and how do you get hold of them if you need them?
- ✔ If you were unclear about something written in these documents, who would be the best person to explain it to you?
- ✔ If the parents or other close relatives of a person you support complained to you about a breach of confidentiality, what would you do about it?
- ✔ If you felt that a colleague had breached confidentiality, how would you handle this?

✔ If you had, by mistake, passed on information that was confidential, what would you do and who would you talk to?

✔ If there was a serious breach of confidentiality in your service, what disciplinary procedures would be taken, and by whom?

If you cannot readily answer questions of this kind, you should refresh your knowledge of the main points of your organisation's policies and procedures on sharing information with others before you go further with this section. If there are any points on which you are unclear, raise them with your line manager.

Practical ways to support and maintain confidentiality

Good practice in relation to confidentiality in the workplace can involve a number of factors that need to become second nature in the way you work.

Confidentiality in day-to-day working

Confidential information about someone can be passed on in a number of ways.

Tips for ensuring confidentiality
In day-to-day working you should:
• respect confidences
• discourage the people you support from giving you personal or private information
• take for granted that something personal is confidential unless the person concerned tells you otherwise
• use the most private and secure means of communicating information that is private and personal.
When confidential information is written you should:
• put confidential papers away safely after using them
• not use faxes
• not use emails unless they are password protected
• make sure you don't leave information on a computer screen open for all to see.
When you talk to anyone about confidential information you should:
• have private conversations, both face-to-face and by telephone, in places where you cannot be overheard
• not refer to matters that are personal to a particular person in groups, whether they are staff or people who use your service
• guide people you work with away from talking about private, family or personal matters in public
• not tell relatives anything that a person with learning disabilities may have told you about private family matters
• be careful about how you phrase confidential information when you have to pass it on to someone else
• not discuss confidential information with colleagues, assuming that they also know about it.

Access to confidential information

An important aspect of confidentiality is checking people's identity to make sure that only authorised people have access to information. There are issues of security and of health and safety involved also. You should be familiar with documents relating to policies and procedures that give guidance on this.

There are several reasons why this is important:

- Passing on information without authorisation is against the rights of an individual.
- It shows lack of respect for the privacy and individuality of the person you support and their family.
- There are legal requirements relating to keeping information confidential.
- Disclosing information can result in intrusion into an individual's private affairs.
- Information can be passed on to other people who should not have access to it.
- It will reflect badly, not only on the person who discloses the information, but also on the service.
- It can make a person the subject of gossip, and can often cause unfounded rumours.

Guidelines to follow before allowing access to confidential information
Assume all personal information is confidential unless you know otherwise.
Never disclose information about people without checking with your line manager unless you have clear authority to do so.
In general, ever disclose possibly confidential information about people over the telephone.
If telephoned information is required urgently, for example by the person's GP or a hospital, check with senior staff if possible and then call the enquirer back on a number that you can check first.
Never disclose private or personal information about a person in a meeting unless given permission to do so by the person, if capable, and your line manager.

Access to people's homes

If you are a support worker who works with people with learning disabilities in their family home, or their own home, you will need to follow the access arrangements agreed in the person's support plan. You must always remember that it is the person's home you are working in and generally you should ring the bell and wait to be allowed in. You should only hold a key to the person's home if

▲ Ring the bell and wait to be allowed in.

there is good reason, and it is clearly laid out in their support plan. If you hold a key to the person's home you should always follow the key-holding policy of your organisation. It is there to ensure that the keys are kept as safe as possible at all times. You should always knock before entering, even if you have a key and the person is unable to answer the door.

The person whose home you are working in always has the right to say who they will have in their home, and you should respect that right. As someone working in the person's home, you should always act honestly and respect their home and property. You should never:

- enter their home when they are not there
- receive gifts or borrow possessions
- use any equipment such as phones, CDs, radios or kettles without permission.

Access to your organisation's premises

You should consider all of the following points before allowing people access to a home or other service run by the organisation you work for:

✔ Always check the identity of anyone seeking entry to the premises.

✔ Ask to see ID with a photograph. Most professionals are trained to offer this from the start, including people from utilities companies, local authorities, etc.

✔ If you find someone wandering around, ask if you can help and accompany them.

✔ Don't allow visitors to wander around unaccompanied unless you have checked that they have the authority to do so.

✔ If you see anyone acting suspiciously, call the manager or a senior member of staff.

✔ If in doubt, make a telephone check to the visitor's organisation, or call the police.

The General Social Care Council (GSCC) is an organisation set up by the government in 2001 to register and regulate all social care workers. It has produced a *Code of Practice* that sets out the standards that all social care workers should work to. It says:

'As a social care worker, you must strive to establish and maintain the trust and confidence of service users and carers. This includes:

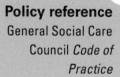

Policy reference
General Social Care
Council *Code of
Practice*

- *being honest and trustworthy*
- *communicating in an appropriate, open, accurate and straightforward way*
- *respecting confidential information and clearly explaining agency policies about confidentiality to service users and carers*
- *being reliable and dependable...'*

Some examples given to illustrate the importance of confidentiality, and the basic principles and practices involved, are quite dramatic. These often tend to stand out and are quickly picked up on and dealt with. On the other hand, it is when dealing with routine day-to-day work that we may slip up and breach confidentiality. Trust is crucial to your relationship with the person you support. If it is lost, even over a small matter, it can cause strong emotional reactions, and it may be a long time before the damage is repaired.

The following account by people with learning disabilities outlines their priorities in respect of confidentiality. As you read it, bear in mind how hurtful a breach of confidence would be to the people concerned.

Example 8: Maintaining confidentiality

Alice keeps her own records separate from any that staff have to keep. These cover things like her health and her finances. She likes this because she chooses to do it, controls it herself and does not have to rely on others for information about her life. She is aware of the need to keep her records safe and confidential and has had staff support her to do so. She has a private place in her own room for these records. She never takes them into public places, such as buses, where they might be lost.

Desmond knew that a full record of his medication was kept and that every time medication was given to him, a staff member had to sign to say it had been done. He looked at his own medication record whenever he wanted to, but no one else could.

The group knew what sorts of records were written about them by staff. These included their medication, doctor's visits, money, accidents and appointments. Staff told the members of the group what was being written about them, and they could read their own records if they wanted to. The entire group regarded what the staff wrote as very personal and private, not to be passed on. Everyone seemed to feel very strongly about this.

In discussion it became clear that privacy, confidentiality and control over their own information were very important to everyone. Indeed, when asked for examples of when confidentiality might be breached they were uncomfortable with the idea that this should ever happen. Staff were aware of adult protection issues, and of the possible need to breach confidentiality if someone might otherwise be put in harm's way. It was clear, though, that this was an issue which would require careful handling by all concerned if it arose.

Think about the following questions, take brief notes of key points and discuss your ideas with a work colleague.

1. What do Alice and Desmond see as important about confidentiality? Can you add anything to this from your own experience with people you support at work?

2. There is a difference of opinion here between the people with learning disabilities and support workers over when confidentiality might be breached. This is perhaps more apparent than real, but it does point to an issue on which you should be clear. What are the two points of view expressed? What would your own approach be as a learning disability worker?

3. Identify practical steps taken in this example to protect confidentiality. What other practical steps might you take in your own work? Are these reflected in the policies and procedures of your organisation? Are close relatives aware of the policies and are they supported to follow them?

4. In any kind of culture, certain approaches are considered to be right and proper, and are carefully maintained. Would you say this service has a culture of confidentiality in that sense?

Now turn to the commentary on this example on page 84.

Commentaries on the examples

At the end of each chapter there is an example and a set of questions for you to answer. The commentaries below highlight the issues that you could have included in your answers. Not everything that can be said about the examples is included. This would take a chapter for each case study on its own. They are designed only to act as guidelines on how to approach each situation. They give examples of how you can use your own practical experiences to describe and comment on your day-to-day experiences.

If you are taking the Induction Award, you'll find that you are asked to describe situations and give examples using your own experience. Familiarity with working on examples will help you with this, although it is how you present and discuss your own knowledge and practical experience that counts in the end.

Example 1: Promoting key values

If you have written in your notes that this is a recipe for disaster, you are not far wrong. Many cases of supposedly challenging behaviour begin in this way. The real challenge from Emma is for her support services to enable her to improve her life in the ways she wants.

But this is not necessarily or entirely the fault of the home staff. The situation in which they and the two older people have been placed is hardly fair to them.

Let's return to basics. Look at the list of nine values at the beginning of the chapter in which this case study appears. If you check systematically through the description you will see that each value has been breached at least once.

In terms of day-to-day practice, you may well feel that some questions need to be asked. Some suggestions follow, but you should have additional ideas of your own.

- Has Emma just been shoehorned into the first available space, regardless of her bereavement and her needs or wishes?
- What about the other two people, facing not only bereavement, but also the disturbance young people tend naturally to bring with them?

- Has any of the three women been given access to counselling of a type and at a level they can understand and benefit from?
- Are the problems in relation to communication largely a matter of shortage of staff time, rather than Emma's disability?
- Do attitudes towards Emma's efforts to stand up for herself and towards possible advocacy seem negative and controlling?
- To what extent do the problems here represent barriers created by services rather than genuine products of Emma's disability?

Now look again at the nine values we have examined. Reflect on how this situation could be improved by working with Emma and the other two women in a way that promotes these values.

Example 2: Respecting diversity, cultures and values

Failure to respect and celebrate the diversity of others can lead to a reduction in the quality of life for everyone. Unfair treatment, bullying and aggression can all stem from such a failure. It tends to be in mixed groups, large or small, that this is recognised. One reason is that we all have something to lose if mutual respect and consideration break down.

On the other hand, we have things to gain from treating each other well. Note how many of the positive aspects mentioned in this example relate to getting more enjoyment out of life. Additional ways of celebrating other cultures can include putting up decorations, sending greetings cards, giving small gifts, special visits from relatives and playing special music.

Example 3: Exploring personal history and preferences

This is a case where some of the information which helped improve things for Jack came from a relatively recent part of his life. Sometimes, though, key facts are buried in the past. What does this say about the need to keep records?

Jack seems alone in the world. But many staff and perhaps volunteers must have worked with him over the years. It may still be possible to contact some of them. Some of those may be willing to help with exploring his personal history and preferences. In addition, his isolation means that extra input is required to find out more about his wishes and needs. Some examples of practical steps that could be taken include giving his key worker more time to chat with him one-to-one, using his preferred communication method, bringing in an advocate if he wants one and looking at what befriending organisations are available in the area.

Example 4: Person-centred working and choice

Note the emphasis on choice in the favourable comments made by the people with learning disabilities on person-centred working. Also note that, as a group, they felt they benefited too. Many of the examples given are directly related to quality of life.

There is only one direct mention here of a negative effect arising from not working in a person-centred way – Cheryl's comment about washing up all the time when she was supposed to be studying catering. There could be many reasons for this – ignorance, laziness or plain exploitation – but it is clear that focusing on the person and her wishes and preferences has had a powerful effect on her life.

Other negative aspects may have to be inferred. For example, Sam sees person-centred planning as having helped him a lot in finding a job he likes, doing what he enjoys for leisure activities and, yet again, in improving his lifestyle. It can be inferred from this that before person-centred working things were less satisfactory.

You may be aware from your own experience that person-centred working and supporting informed choice demands a lot of staff time. This can be a problem in developing and continuing person-centred approaches across the board, but has to be weighed against the obvious advantages of such ways of working for all concerned.

Example 5: Using Elliott's support plan

Rosie and Paul should see Elliott's support plan as the key document for informing the type of support Paul provides as a volunteer. The support plan will set out the areas where Elliott needs support and experiences, skills and knowledge he is seeking to gain. The support plan will help Paul to focus the support he provides on the areas set out in the plan such as helping Elliott to pay for tickets on his own, finding his seat and choosing and buying refreshments.

At the review meetings every three months with Elliott and his key worker, Rosie and Paul can discuss Elliott's progress in the areas he is seeking to focus on. Elliott and Paul can say how things have gone in the three areas that are important to Elliott. The review can help Elliott and his key worker decide if his support plan needs to be changed or updated.

Example 6: Recognising the right to take risks

You might have included the following in your answers.

The Beech Tree Centre

The negative consequences include making people dependent, not taking account of individual needs and differences, denying people new opportunities, stopping them learning new things or meeting new people, restricting their lives, and possibly creating frustration, which might lead to challenging behaviours. They are also denying people their right to control their own lives and make their own decisions, even if sometimes they make mistakes or run into difficulties, as we all do in the normal process of running our own lives and which we take for granted.

This approach can be described as overprotective and restrictive. However well meant, it denies people the chance to grow and develop in their own individual way. But some people and many families find such an approach comforting because of the built-in high safety element. It can also have advantages for family carers in heavily reducing the amount of time they have to spend on providing care, thus helping with employment and other activities.

The Four Acres Centre

Potential benefits include developing independence, new opportunities for learning, choice and decision-making, a sense of achievement, learning new skills, making new friendships, managing their own lives and variety in their lives. Potential hazards include exploitation, loneliness, discrimination and failure, as well as more uncertainty and possibly increased support from family carers who are also entitled to choice and control over their lives.

The approach here is one of risk-taking on the basis of assessment and management of risk. It is also one of developing empowerment through providing the social environment in which barriers are lowered so that people can seek their fair share of power and control over their own lives.

Example 7: Using risk assessment procedures

There are some positive aspects to this support plan. It is aimed at giving Leah greater freedom and control. Also, it is realistic about what Leah can achieve within a given time, and it breaks learning down into tasks she can accomplish without unnecessary risk. But beyond this the assessment is in fact careless.

It is part of good risk assessment procedures to specify ways of dealing with the negative consequences of any risks that have been identified. This applies not only to actual risks, that is the ones which are present and obvious, but also to potential, and less obvious, problems.

This has not been done in the depth needed to ensure risk is controlled and kept to a minimum. What would happen, for example, if there was a bus strike one day or if the bus Leah usually caught didn't turn up? Would she stand there for hours, try to walk, take another bus or just go home? What would Leah do if she ran into trouble on the bus or at the bus stop, through bullying or sexual harassment, for example?

A more thorough risk assessment would have gone beyond the immediate situation to identify these and other potential risks and make contingency plans. We can think of this as the 'what if' approach. What if the bus breaks down? What if Leah misses the bus? What if she doesn't have the right change or feels ill or frightened?

By identifying as many potential risks as possible we are not being negative, but rather seeking to reduce negative consequences. Once risks are known, action can be taken to remove them or reduce their effects and to prepare Leah to cope with them. And if this takes a little longer it is surely worth it to give her the best possible support in taking this step towards greater control of her life.

Example 8: Maintaining confidentiality

Confidentiality is still sometimes viewed as a staff-only issue, something that we take care of for service users. The usefulness of the case studies here is that they emphasise the huge importance that people with learning disabilities attach to confidentiality about their personal lives and information, and the way in which many people wish to take it under their own control.

If we look back at the values examined at the beginning of this book, many of them, especially privacy, involve confidentiality when put into practice. Dignity and respect would be hard to maintain for long in an environment that lacked confidentiality in working with service users. Accidental breaches of confidentiality can not only be wounding, but can also make it difficult to continue working closely with someone.

Sometimes, however, confidentiality has to be breached quite deliberately. These occasions are likely to be familiar to you from your training and practical experience in risk assessment, and will involve possible differences of opinion between staff and service users over duty of care. The example picked out here is that of abuse. If issues relating to the protection of vulnerable people arise, support staff may have to seriously consider consultation over breaching confidentiality.

A key point here is that the assumption is always in favour of maintaining confidentiality. A breach should be considered only as a last resort, on the basis of consultation that will normally include the service user, and in the service user's best interests.

In emergencies, of course, it may not be possible to spend much time on consultation. Because of this, it is useful to have discussed issues of confidentiality with service users in advance, and to have made it clear when confidences might have to be broken. To do this effectively and to maintain trust and good relationships requires what is known as a culture of confidentiality of the type that certainly seems to exist in the home described in this example.

Glossary

advocacy speaking up for yourself or speaking up for someone else

advocate an independent person who supports someone to speak up for themselves

alternative and augmentative communication different methods to help people with learning disabilities communicate that are tailored for individuals and used instead of or to supplement speech, including signing and gesture; and electronic systems that may use symbols and offer artificial speech

Code of Practice a UK document for social care workers setting out the standards they should work to

confidentiality concerning things that need to be kept private

direct payments funding received directly from a local council, so that people can organise their own social care support

discriminate treat unfairly, often because of a person's race, religion or sex

diversity differences in ethnicity, religion, sex and culture

empowerment a shift in the balance of power so that people with learning disabilities can make their own decisions and take control of their own lives

family carer a relative of a person with learning disabilities who has an interest in their well-being

General Social Care Council the organisation that regulates the social care workforce in England and sets the standards of care through the Codes of Practice

hazard anything that could cause harm to a person

health action plan a support plan that sets out a person's health needs and how they should be met

induction a period of learning, shortly after starting a new job or volunteering placement

life story book an account of a person's life, including stories and memories of past events, relationships and experiences that make us who we are

person-centred approaches   a way of working every day with people with learning disabilities that puts the person and their dreams at the centre of everything you do

policy   a statement or plan of action that clearly sets out an organisation's position or approach on a particular issue and tells staff what should be done in the circumstances

prejudice   negative value judgements or opinions about someone

rights   a framework of laws that protects people from harm and guarantees them basic entitlements, such as the right to respect, equality and a fair trial

risk   how likely it is for a hazard to cause harm

risk assessment   identifying and documenting possible risks and deciding how to manage them

services   the provision of social care support for a person in their own home, their local community, a residential home or similar place

support plan   a detailed plan of a person's support needs that support workers should use to inform their day-to-day support for that individual

total communication   using the best methods for an individual, always in conjunction with speech, according to how they communicate in various environments, including drawing, pictures and photos; writing and symbols; signing; body language expressions and gestures; tone and pattern of voice; and objects of reference

Mapping to NVQ Health & Social Care Knowledge Specifications

Chapter 1: Promoting person-centred values

HSC24		HSC234	
1, 2, 5, 7, 8, 12		1, 2, 3, 4, 5, 6, 7, 8	

HSC35	HSC3111	HSC3116
1, 2, 3, 4, 5, 6, 7, 8, 15, 16, 22	1, 2, 3, 4, 5, 6, 9, 13, 14, 15, 16, 17, 18, 20	1, 2, 3, 4, 5, 6, 8, 9, 11, 14, 15, 17

Links to other units: HSC21, HSC23, HSC25, HSC27, HSC233, HSC31, HSC33, HSC328, HSC329, HSC366, HSC368, HSC3114

Chapter 2: Respecting diversity, cultures and values

HSC24		HSC234	
1, 2, 4, 5, 6, 7, 8, 12, 14		1, 2, 3, 4, 6, 7	

HSC35	HSC3111	HSC3116
1, 2, 3, 4, 5, 6, 12, 15	1, 2, 3, 4, 5, 6, 14, 16, 20	1, 2, 3, 4, 5, 6, 7, 11, 15, 16, 17, 18, 19, 20, 21, 22

Links to other units: HSC21, HSC27, HSC31, HSC329, HSC350

Chapter 3: Understanding personal history and preferences

HSC21	HSC24	HSC234		
2, 3, 5, 6, 7, 8, 10, 13, 14	2, 6, 9, 12, 13, 14, 21	3		

HSC31	HSC35	HSC328	HSC329	HSC3111
2, 3, 4, 5, 6, 7, 9, 10, 13, 14, 15	2, 4, 6, 7, 16, 23	2, 4, 5, 6, 12	2, 5, 16	2, 4, 7, 15, 17, 19, 20

Links to other units: HSC25, HSC27, HSC227, HSC233, HSC368, HSC3114, HSC3116

Chapter 4: Working in a person-centred way

HSC21	HSC24	HSC234			
2, 3, 8, 9, 12	2, 3, 4, 6, 8, 11, 14, 20	3, 4, 5, 8			

HSC31	HSC35	HSC328	HSC329	HSC3111	HSC3114
2, 9, 10, 11, 12, 13, 14, 15	2, 3, 4, 6, 8, 16, 23	2, 3, 4, 5, 10, 12, 13	1, 2, 4, 5, 6, 7, 16, 18	2, 3, 4, 6, 15, 17, 19, 20, 21	2, 3, 4, 5, 16, 17, 18

Links to other units: HSC27, HSC227, HSC233, HSC240, HSC335, HSC395, HSC3116

Chapter 5: Using support plans

HSC21		HSC25	
2, 3, 5, 8, 10, 12, 14		5, 6, 8, 9	

HSC31	HSC328	HSC329
2, 5, 19	2, 6, 7, 8, 10, 11, 12, 13, 15, 16	2, 8, 10, 16, 18, 21, 22

Links to other units: HSC23, HSC24, HSC27, HSC233, HSC33, HSC35, HSC3114

Chapter 6: The right to take risks

HSC24		HSC234		
2, 3, 5, 8, 9, 14		2, 3, 4, 5		

HSC35	HSC329	HSC335	HSC395	HSC3111
2, 3, 4, 7, 16	2, 4, 5, 7, 16	2, 3, 4, 5, 6, 7, 20, 21	2, 3, 4, 5, 6, 7, 20, 21	2, 3, 4, 7, 17, 21

Links to other units: HSC22, HSC27, HSC211, HSC227, HSC233, HSC240, HSC32, HSC3114

Chapter 7: Risk assessment

HSC21		HSC24		HSC240	
4, 5, 10, 12, 13, 14		2, 3, 8, 9, 15, 16, 17, 18, 21		1, 4, 5	

HSC32	HSC35	HSC328	HSC329	HSC335	HSC395
2, 3, 4, 14	1, 6, 7, 8, 16, 17, 20, 23	5, 6, 8, 11, 12, 13, 15, 16	6, 7, 10, 15, 16, 20, 21, 22	1, 5, 6, 17	1, 5, 6, 7, 17, 28

Links to other units: HSC22, HSC25, HSC27, HSC227, HSC233, HSC234, HSC31, HSC3111, HSC3114

Chapter 8: Principles and practice of confidentiality

HSC21		HSC24		HSC234	
1, 4, 5, 10, 11, 13, 14		2, 4, 9, 18, 21		1, 2, 4, 8	

HSC31	HSC35	HSC328	HSC335	HSC3111
1, 4, 5, 14, 17	1, 3, 7, 20	1, 3, 6, 15	1, 2, 3, 6, 17, 26	1, 3, 4, 20

Links to other units: HSC22, HSC25, HSC27, HSC229, HSC233, HSC240, HSC32, HSC395, HSC3114

Resources

Publications

Books on practice

Baum, S., Lynggaard H. (eds) 2006. *Intellectual Disabilities – A Systemic Approach*. London: Karnac Books

Bradley, A. 2006. *Personal Development and Reflective Practice in a Learning Disability Service*. Kidderminster: BILD

Cambridge, P. and Carnaby, S. (eds) 2005. *Person Centred Planning and Care Management with People with Learning Disabilities*. London: Jessica Kingsley

Concannon, L. 2005. *Planning for Life: Involving adults with learning disabilities in service planning*. Abingdon: Routledge

Hollins, S. and Hollins, M. 2005. *You and Your Child – Making Sense of Learning Disabilities*. London: Karnac Books

Lawton, A. 2006. *A Voice of Their Own*. Kidderminster: BILD

Leece, J., Bornat, J. (eds) 2006. *Developments in Direct Payments*. Oxford: The Policy Press

Mansell, J. 2004. *Person Centred Active Support*. Brighton: Pavilion

Pearce, J. 2006. *Person Centred Planning in a Learning Disability Service*. Kidderminster: BILD

Powell, S. 2005. *Risk in Challenging Behaviour – A good practice guide for professionals*. Kidderminster: BILD

Publications on policy and the law

An Easy Guide to the Human Rights Act can be found at www.valuingpeople.gov.uk/Rights.htm

Department of Health. 2001. *Valuing People – A New Strategy for Learning Disability for the 21st Century*. Norwich: The Stationery Office

Fanstone, C. and Andrews, S. 2005. *Learning Disabilities, Sex and the Law*. London: Family Planning Association

HM Government. 2006. *The Government's Annual Policy on Learning Disability 2005 – Valuing People: Making Things Better*. London: The Stationery Office

Hughes, A. and Coombs, P. 2001. *Easy Guide to the Human Rights Act 1998*. Kidderminster: BILD

Mental Capacity Act 2005. London: The Stationery Office

Ruebain, D. and Graham, J.-A. 2005. *Disability Discrimination Act Toolkit (10th edn)*. London: Inclusion Distribution

Scottish Executive. 2000. *The Same As You? A review of services for people with learning disabilities*. Edinburgh: The Stationery Office

VIA. 2005. *One Law for All? – The Impact of the Human Rights Act on People with Learning Difficulties*. London: Values into Action

Audio-visual

After Life – the 2004 film starring Paula Sage which raises important issues about learning disabilities in society.
Website: www.sodapictures.com

Creative Conversations – a video aimed at supporting communication with people who have severe and profound learning disabilities.
Website: www.pavpub.com

Life is My Own, Life is for Living – A DVD and handbook about 14 people who are successfully using direct payments to take control of their own support services and live independently.
Penderels Trust: www.penderelstrust.org.uk

Look at the Way We Live – A short film that shows how three self-advocates deal with their housing and support options.
Penderels Trust: www.penderelstrust.org.uk

My Home, My Rights, My Choices – a video, handbook and picture cards about making choices in everyday life.
The Langstone Society Tel: 01384 243665

My Life Plan: An Interactive Resource for Person Centred Planning – A CD-ROM using the latest software techniques to enable people with learning disabilities to take more control of the person-centred planning process.
Information Plus: www.information-plus.co.uk

The Right to be You – A DVD that informs and empowers service users in finding support for their choices.
Ealing Consortium: www.ealing.org.uk

Supported Living – Train the Trainers Pack – for training staff in supporting independent living.
Website: www.paradigm-uk.org

What's Right for Me? – A CD that helps people with learning disabilities understand how to use direct payments to increase their independence.
Penderels Trust: www.penderelstrust.org.uk

Useful websites

British Institute of Learning Disabilities: www.bild.org.uk
includes a guide to other useful websites and information about
the Common Induction Standards

Foundation for People with Learning Disabilities: www.fpwld.org.uk

General Social Care Council:
   www.gscc.org.uk (England)
   www.niscc.info (Northern Ireland)
   www.sssc.uk.com (Scotland
   www.ccwales.org.uk (Wales)

Mencap: www.mencap.org.uk

National Family Carer Network: www.familycarers.org.uk

Office of Public Sector Information: www.opsi.gov.uk
includes information about Acts of Parliament

Paradigm: www.paradigm-uk.org

Index

qualifications vi–viii

racial discrimination 18
reading tips xii
reassessment, support plans 45–6
religion
    diversity of 14
    Jewish holy days/festivals 21
resources xi
respect 6–7
    practical ways of showing 20–3
reviews
    of risk assessments 67–9
    of support plans 46
rights 3–4
    promoting 10–11
    supporting 36
risk-taking 35
    avoiding unnecessary 55–6
    benefits of 53–6
    current attitudes 53
    and duty of care 51–2
    historical attitudes 49
    negative effects of overprotection 49–50
    reasons for discouraging 50–3
    right to take risks 48, 56–7, 83
    social barriers to 50–1
risk assessment
    and confidentiality 66–7
    informing others 63, 64–7
    keeping records 65–6
    main principles of 59
    policies and procedures 52–3, 59
    reporting 64–5
    reviewing 67–9
    unplanned risks 62–3
    updating 67–9
    using procedures 60–2, 69–70, 84
    who to involve in 63–4
risk management 59–61

self-directed support 32
services 2
sex discrimination 18–19
sign language 37, 38
social barriers to risk-taking 50–1
social care workers, Code of Practice 9, 78
standards in social care 9, 78
study skills xi–xvi
support plans 20–1, 41
    checking cycle 46
    day-to-day support 44–6
    effect of life changes 42–3
    planning cycle 45
    support worker role 47, 82
support workers
    access to people's homes 76–7
    role in support plans 47, 82

terminology ix
time management xiii–xiv
total communication 25

unplanned risks
    dealing with 62–3
    recording decisions 66

values
    choice 5
    dignity 6
    equal opportunities 9
    independence 6
    individuality 2
    partnership 7–8
    privacy 5
    promoting 10–11, 80–1
    respect 6–7
    rights 3–4
Valuing People (DOH White Paper) 18, 32

websites xv–xvi
wishes see preferences